Mix Marriage

The Diary of
a Portuguese Bride

Elizabeth Cadell

The Friendly Air Publishing
thefriendlyairpublishing.com

Part 1

Saturday April 15th.

Today bought my wedding dress. Mother came up on an early train; met her at Waterloo and we toured the bridal departments. Found them surprisingly full; assumed other brides-to-be girls like myself, working in London and free only on Saturdays. Other mothers all looked up-from-the-country, like mine. Lassooed salesgirl, and by process of financial elimination arrived swiftly at final choice between satin (with train) and lace (without). I preferred the lace but Mother said very difficult to make it up into anything after the wedding, and style of satin more suited to my figure. Salesgirl tactfully withdrew while Mother and I argued it out, but returned to say sorry, mistake in price of satin, as she had unfortunately read the price tag upside down; price of dress not £19 but £61. Therefore bought lace, also long veil and small filigree tiara; studied myself in long glass as fitter fitted, and thought healthy glow inappropriate, as brides ought to look ethereal. Drove back to flat with Mother, progress punctuated by stops for Mother to collect two pairs of my shoes from mender's, two dresses of mine from cleaner's, two weeks laundry, also to pay grocery bill and leave rent cheque at house agent's. Mother very annoyed and said that it was Too Bad the way I held up all this sort of thing as soon as I knew she was coming up to London. Now no money left to take me out to lunch. Had lunch at flat, eggs and salad; also dinner; salad and cheese. Philippa not in; Mother asked where she was and I said she was staying with the Welbys in Kent for the weekend; omitted to mention that only Francis Welby there, as Mother hearing disquieting rumours in village and beginning to wonder if Philippa really the ideal flat-mate she once thought her.

Sunday April 16th.

Went with Mother to Holy Communion at Westminster Abbey and enjoyed it, but Mother abstracted on way home and throughout breakfast; then came out of reverie to say that as wedding getting near, it was useless to go on evading issues and avoiding relations; it would be far better to take bull by horns and disclose the true facts. She added that in any case, Uncle George (bull), on hearing from Aunt Freda of announcement in *The Times,* had cut short his fishing holiday and was due home tomorrow. In this event, best thing to do would be to ring up Aunt Freda and ask her to come and lunch with us in town before going on to the station to meet Uncle George. I said this was a good idea but that it would be better for Mother to stay at the flat for the night in order to avoid coming up on same train as Aunt Freda. This arranged; Aunt Freda phoned to, time and place fixed.

Monday April 17th.

Aunt Freda came up and met Mother and self for lunch at Simpson's. Atmosphere not friendly. Aunt Freda opened by saying that very hard on all members of the family to open their *Times* all unsuspecting, and read announcement without any preparation whatsoever; if Mother and I thought other, more distant members of family not entitled to courtesy or consideration, very well, but Uncle George had always been second father to me, and if natural affection not enough on my part, surely his position as Head Of Family entitled him to pre-announcement knowledge of the fact that his niece was about to marry a Portuguese nobody had ever heard of. Pause to order food. Talk general over sole and salad; then Aunt Freda asked when and where I was to be married. Mother said Saturday June 3rd, at the little new church they'd just built in the village. Aunt Freda said you mean the Catholic one? Mother said yes. Aunt Freda said that coming from Portugal, and with name like that, of course he would be. She asked Mother when I was likely to want the cottage; if we (Mother and I) hadn't preserved this ridiculous secrecy about the affair, Uncle George could have set about giving the tenants notice long ago. Mother said no need to give tenants notice. Aunt Freda said would she (Mother) for once use her head; how could the tenants be got out without notice? Mother said tenants needn't be got out. Pause for Aunt Freda to take this in. Did Mother, she asked slowly at last, mean to sit there and tell her that I considered a delightful cottage in the country, within daily reach of London, not good enough for young couple starting out in life ? Yes, couldn't be nicer, Mother said, but as a matter of fact, my husband and I would not be living in England; we were going to live in Portugal.

Terrible scene, *sotto voce* on account of waiters and near-by lunchers. We had obviously got her up here, Aunt Freda said, to tell her this in the hope that she would break it to Uncle George. Did we realise, did we have the ghost of an idea of what he was going to say, how he was going to behave, when he knew? It was all very well for Mother to sit there and look pained; the one who was going to be pained was the one who had to tell Uncle George. Mother was only his sister, but she, Freda, had the misfortune to be his wife. First we play a miserable trick on everybody and say not a word about my engagement to a man with a name like an ice-cream seller's, and then we get her up here and calmly tell her I don't want the house Uncle George set aside for me and kept for me in spite of the fact that it would have been very useful indeed to his own daughters when they married. I said I was sorry, but nothing I could do about it. This intervention a mistake, as guns immediately trained on me. This, Aunt Freda told me, was what came of being allowed to go abroad at the age of seventeen to Continental families nobody knew anything about. This was what came of getting out of touch with one's own country. She, Aunt Freda, had hitherto given me credit for a little sense, but this proved I hadn't a grain—and as for gratitude ! At this point, she called for the bill (her share), paid it and left. I said wouldn't you have thought the row would have been over religion and not over a cottage? Mother said no; junior branch of family skipped out during Reformation and returned solidly Catholic, so that no problem. Real problem this cottage, which Uncle George put aside for me shortly after being appointed godfather, and which, Mother said, Aunt Freda had been after ever since; the idea that I didn't want it after all the rows she and Uncle George had had over it was going to upset them both very much. I said one of the most attractive things about marrying and going far away was that I would be saved from the prospect of having to settle down less than three miles away from Uncle George. Mother said I hadn't heard the last of it yet by any means. I drove her to the station and told her I was going to give a fortnight's notice at the office at the end of the week, and come home. She said that would be nice, and asked what about finding another girl to share flat with Philippa. I said had already discussed this with Philippa, who was willing to keep flat on and find somebody else to share; didn't add that this likely to be Francis Welby. Just before train left, Mother said why didn't I ask poor Clara Cornhill to be one of my bridesmaids. This took my breath away; said I'd had more than enough of Clara all my life; had never at any time wanted to be friend of hers, but had never at any time been able to shake her off. I had had her round my neck throughout our schooldays, and had had the greatest difficulty in preventing her from moving into the flat when she heard I'd got one in London. Mother said poor thing, meaning Clara; only child, dreadful parents, nothing in the way of looks, no charm, no young men, no parties. At this point, train left and I walked to car thinking of Clara Cornhill and agreeing that life hadn't done much for her up to now, but nothing I could do.

Tuesday April 18th.

Telephone call from Mother during breakfast, warning me Uncle George coming up to London to call on me. Thanked her and said I would arrange to spend evening out. Just after lunch, office boy came up and told me gentleman calling himself my uncle downstairs in waiting room. Felt this office-storming completely unethical and went down to tell Uncle George so, but Uncle George got in first salvo and several subsequent ones and said forcibly that I didn't know what I was doing and it was his duty to point out and so here he was, pointing out. He said it all came of my having no father, and a mother who'd had no more sense than to let me loose in France and Spain and Italy getting my ideas out of focus. Foreign languages his foot; his own daughters married at twenty speaking nothing but plain English, and got decent Englishmen with Christian names and were settled in their own country where they belonged, with a couple of sturdy English children and not a series or string of swarthy Portuguese. He wasn't surprised the fellow was a Catholic; he'd always suspected my mother of having Leanings, but how she could so far forget herself and her duty as to let me go off with him was more than he could get over. There must be something wrong somewhere, or we wouldn't have hidden the fellow away like that instead of fetching him out and letting people take a look at him. Things had gone pretty far, but it was not too late to make me listen to a bit of horse sense. Horse paused for air. I had intended to say something about being grateful for the cottage, but found myself telling him *(a)* that he could bully Mother, but not me; *(b)* no business to invade my office and shout; loved Afonso very much. This last a mistake, as name acted like red rag and made bull bellow; roared: "My God, *Afonso* ! Do you mean to tell me you're going to leave your home and your country to go off with a ruddy Portugoose called Afonso?" I said yes, I was. He said he had never in all his life heard such twaddle, and why couldn't the fellow stay here, where I belonged? Did I understand that I was proposing to go to a country, to a way of life no healthy English girl capable of standing for a week let alone a lifetime? Asked him to keep his opinions to himself until he'd learned something about Portugal or the Portuguese, and added that am twenty-six and not sixteen, and quite capable of managing my own affairs. Uncle George asked what more sensible than settling down in that splendid little cottage; wasn't this fellow able to hold down a job in this country? I said I was going to do as every other wife did: go with my husband, stay with my husband; added was stunned by narrow and insular reaction to my engagement, but if my relations didn't want to come to my wedding, their presents would do just as well as their presence. At this Uncle George took departure, almost knocking down my boss on way out, and not stopping to apologise. Boss looked after him and said: "Relation of yours?" and I said "Yes." He said he knew I'd catch it; why wouldn't I call the whole thing off and marry him as he'd asked me to? Thanked him, and said I happened to love my fiancé. He said Nonsense, a girl who'd had the pick of so many fine upstanding Northerners, himself included, couldn't possibly settle for a black-visaged guy named Adolpho. *Afonso.* Well, that was worse, he said, and how about this twelve-in-the-family business ? No birth control clinics in Portugal; the Pope wouldn't hear of such a thing; I ought really to think again. Said I had thought again and again—and again, and if he'd go upstairs and sign the morning's letters, I'd get on with the next batch.

Got home at 5.40, to find that Philippa, who up to now had backed me, was having qualms; Francis had told her that Portuguese women not at all Advanced, not to say Cloistered, and better if I thought again. I said better if Francis minded his own business. After supper tried to ring up Afonso in Paris; no reply. Went to bed and howled.

Friday April 21st.

Letter from Paris, from Antoinette; delighted to be bridesmaid. Came home from office to find evidence that the landlady had once again come up from basement quarters to have stealthy snoop. Heard her mounting stairs after supper and put on icy face before opening the door; determined not to let her set foot inside. She asked if we would put rubbish bin out earlier in mornings: I said sorry, quite impossible unless went down in dressing gown and ran gauntlet of crude young men on middle floor. Denied that arm of chair in drawing room damaged through sitting on. Said springs of sofa sagging when we came, and had pointed same out to Agent. Denied banging doors, talking loudly on landing and waking other tenants when returning late at night. Refused to disclose name of owner of yellow sports car that flashed headlights into her bedroom window. Lost temper, said please leave, banged door. Wondered if I was growing violent, like Uncle George.

Telephone call from Aunt Mary to say that Uncle George had been talking to her and she was feeling uneasy and would like a little chat; perhaps if she came up from Haywards Heath one day I could meet her and give her dinner, just a small, very light dinner in the flat. I said with great though false enthusiasm that this very good plan, but before I could be pinned down to a date, the pips went and Aunt Mary faded out, never in the history of telephones having been known to overstay the first pip. Put receiver down and wondered why so many rich people so miserly; probably cause and effect. Remembered that Aunt Mary hadn't yet got round to giving me a 21st birthday present, although she is one of my godmothers. Philippa came in; she said the landlady had waylaid her as she came in, and had been very rude. Occurred to me that in snooping round our flat, landlady must have come across several odds and ends of property belonging to Francis, and drawn catty but correct conclusion. Went to meet Afonso at the airport at

7.30. Took a long, clear look at him and thought he made every other male passenger look tepid, undersized and effete. Kissed him as usual, but he asked what was the matter. I said nothing, only relations, and he said he knew a wonderful restaurant in Jermyn Street where no relations permitted to intrude. Went there, and after onion soup and lobster and zabaglione felt strong enough to recount interview with Uncle George. Afonso said he quite understood his reaction; he would have felt like that himself if I'd refused a house he offered me, and went away. We agreed that it had been a mistake not to have exhibited him at the very beginning, but I said perhaps Mother's idea of springing the announcement on everybody and saving argument was easier in the long run. After discussion, decided to have a party at the flat and invite all my relations to meet Afonso. Afonso not enchanted at this prospect, but agreed must be got through. On way home, he told me that his parents arriving by air on May 9th.

Saturday April 22nd.

Had arranged to clean flat with Philippa, but she left at dawn with Francis for unknown destination. Did it myself but managed to rope Afonso in for the heavy bits when he came to call for me to drive me home for the weekend. Found him ham-handed to a degree, but reminded myself that he had never in the whole course of his life had to lift a finger, having been surrounded by scores of servants. Drove down to the cottage, and being encouraged by the warmth of the day, stopped to buy sandwiches and a bottle of wine; sun vanished, rain poured down, had picnic inside car. Afonso staying for weekend.

Sunday April 23rd.

Mother and I went to Protestant, Afonso to Catholic Church. Rest of day spent by me lying in long chair in garden, and by Afonso in mowing lawn, mending puncture in plastic chair, fixing up new clothes line, oiling garage door, fixing leak in bathroom shower, weeding flower beds and mending spare room bedside lamp. Said he did all this out of love, not of me but of Mother.

Monday April 24th.

Gave two weeks' notice and boss turned unexpectedly sour; said he had never thought I'd go through with it, and that somebody ought to stop me before too late. Caught me off guard and enfolded me in his arms and said why wouldn't I marry him. Didn't like to remind him that question of marrying him hadn't come up until I got engaged to Afonso; previous proposals all definitely dishonourable.

Letter from Madrid, from Inez: would love to be bridesmaid and would love to come to England, but not allowed to come without her brother, so was coming with him.

Went to Old Girls' Dinner held in dreary restaurant near King's Cross. Pouring rain, no taxis, no answer from Afonso's flat when I phoned in desperation to ask him to drive me there. Joined long bus queue and arrived at restaurant late, mud-splashed and in no mood for auld lang syne. Dreaded being cornered by Clara Cornhill, but learned with relief that her grandfather just died, and O.G. Dinner felt too festive for spirit of mourning. Looking round at the assembly, felt I couldn't agree with this. Spirits further depressed by long and pointless speeches, and lid put on Reunion after dinner, when every O.G. of my class, without exception, said she couldn't understand my marrying a foreigner. Tried without success to keep my replies civil. Home by bus, feeling grateful to Mother for having made up so handsomely in later years for the time I spent at an English boarding school, public.

Cried in bed, for no special reason.

Tuesday April 25th.

Wrote and posted party invitations for Saturday May 6th.

Wednesday April 26th.

Got a cheque from a great-aunt in New Zealand and took the afternoon off to spend it. Bought, among other things, table cloths, table mats and some china. Afonso came to supper, inspected purchases and said all very nice, but all better and cheaper in Portugal. He also said electric toaster and little electric fan very nice, but unfortunately no electricity where we were going to live. Was staggered by this, and asked why he hadn't said so before. He said he had, several times; again and again, in fact. He asked if I was quite, quite sure I knew where I was going and what I was doing. I said that I wanted to be where he was, doing what he was doing, even without electricity. He said that, strangely, this didn't make him feel any less worried. Discussed honeymoon plans, got nowhere.

Sunday April 30th.

Drove down with Afonso to have lunch with godmother—not Aunt Mary, but favourite one. Lovely sunny day; enjoyed the drive, and Afonso much impressed by house and extensive woodland setting. Lovely lunch, lovely godmother. Told her I wished my blood relations, with exception of Mother, half as nice as her. She said that what I liked was the Irish in her, but that my own relations were fine old English stock, insular perhaps, not intellectual, but staunch and strong and reliable and honest and unyielding; one had to take the good with the bad, and I must always be proud of my heritage. I asked Afonso if he was listening, and he said he was. Godmother asked what we'd like as a wedding present, and I said that according to Afonso, everything better and cheaper in Portugal, but I would like some of those terribly expensive linen sheets in pastel shades that never faded and lasted a hundred years; Godmother said she would arrange this. She took me aside to say Afonso very fine young man but looked sensitive and I must look after him. Promised I would.

Monday May 1st.

Woke up feeling Queen-of-Mayish, but this rapidly dispelled by atmosphere at office; boss spent morning interviewing prospective successors; pronounced them all hopeless, and said he realised I had to leave to get married, but didn't see why I had to leave him in the lurch so long before the ceremony. Worked late in a sort of futile effort to make amends; Afonso very angry, called for me and drove me down to old and very nice pub on Portsmouth Road; beer and sandwiches; place almost to ourselves, very restful. Afonso asked why I was suddenly keeping a diary, and I told him it was on account of what Dr. Johnson told Boswell—to *"yield me great satisfaction when the particulars had faded from my remembrance."* Explained further that I had lately felt a great surge of interest in Mother's past: her engagement, her marriage, where and how fallen in love with father, what sort of sex life, what kind of birth control, since only one child in eight years before widowhood. Had failed to get out of her any single fact; her answers simply to the effect that she had forgotten, as it was all so long ago. Afonso said he thought probing into her intimate past unwarrantable curiosity; disagreed with this at the time, but wondered about it afterwards. Discussed honeymoon plans, got nowhere.

Tuesday May 2nd.

Got home from office to find Neil Bruce on doorstep waiting for me. Took him upstairs and learned he'd got special leave in order to have one last try at making me change my mind and marry him. Found it terribly hard to say I wouldn't. Looked at him and knew with certainty that I'd never find a nicer, cleaner, stronger type of Englishman ... Scotsman. Big, healthy, good, patient and kind. And rich and un-spoilt and devoted. Tried not to cry but couldn't help it; managed to say I was quite, quite sure about not loving him. He said if things didn't turn out well, I could be sure he'd be there to turn to, and I thanked him. He said that was all, and went away, and I went on crying and was still at it when Afonso arrived. Efforts to comfort me unavailing. He said that long engagements were a great mistake, not to say a strain on both parties. I said anybody who called two months a long engagement was out of their mind, and if he meant what I thought he meant, I personally was under no strain whatsoever; added that I didn't feel like going out, and as there was no food in the flat there was no point in his staying. He asked if the thought of meeting his parents was upsetting me, and I asked why in Heaven's name he couldn't forget himself and his fatuous family for a while. He said no need to shout, his parents weren't as bad as that and there was no need for me to be frightened. At this, lost wool completely and told him a couple of Portuguese parents couldn't frighten a girl who'd coped with Uncle George all her life; I then asked him who he thought they were, anyhow? He said he'd left something in his car, and came back with ham, tongue, potato salad, black olives, chicken sandwiches, cheese sandwiches and mixed pickles from the delicatessen down the road. Looked in the cupboard for beer but found Francis had drunk it; walked down the road with Afonso and bought a bottle of wine. After supper, told him what I'd been crying about and entirely ruined the evening: Afonso's spirits dropped to zero because, he said, could not help putting himself in the other man's place and knowing how he felt. Sent him home early and went to bed and cried, probably out of sheer habit.

Wednesday May 3rd.

Boss away, so went home early. Washed hair and set it and heard Philippa come in. Called to her; no answer. Went into drawing room and straight into big row. I had obviously, she said, talked to my mother about her and Francis and my mother had obviously talked to her parents; nobody else knew of the affair. Now all out, her family raising Cain and trying to get her home. I replied to this by saying *(a)* I had never said anything to my mother and *(b)* my mother had a lot of faults, but giving people away wasn't one of them and *(c)* far from affair being secret, neither Philippa nor Francis had ever taken the slightest trouble to be discreet, and the village had been seething with rumours for weeks. Philippa shouted discreet about what, did I think they were ashamed of it? If so, I was mistaken; they didn't care who knew. I said in that case, why upset over parents, and she said what else but money? Had we ever been able to live in this flat on our salaries? What would we have done if we hadn't been bailed out every now and then by our parents? Now strong pressure being brought to bear to make her go home and stay home; she'd rather die. She said she knew she had no hope of getting any sympathy from me, as it was only too clear I'd never approved of Francis; my views were archaic to say the least, and trouble with me had always been that I wanted every man who looked at me to rush out and buy a marriage licence before so much as holding my hand; trouble with me was that in spite of this thin and very boring international veneer I'd acquired since becoming fluent in French and Spanish and Italian, I was still, mentally, where I'd started, in a God-forsaken village on the Sussex Downs where only cows and bulls and yokels admitted or permitted to have sex life. She would like to say, now that she'd raised the subject, that a little sex life wouldn't have done me any harm, and if I'd lived a normal life instead of an inhibited one, perhaps I wouldn't have been so keen to turn down offers from eligible Englishmen and rush off with a foreigner. And it was all very well to look down my nose at people having affairs, but if men couldn't afford to marry a girl, what did she have to do? Live like a nun until a stray millionaire dropped in? Trouble with me was that I had an ice-cold nature and it was therefore useless to talk to me of anything relating to sex. She then went into her room, banged door, came out later with suitcase and said she had decided that she would not, after all, be a bridesmaid. Also, as so short a time now left before my leaving the flat, she would move out and return when I'd gone. Front door banged behind her and I was left with the feeling that she must have been on the boil for some time, and perhaps I'd been tactless to be so happy in front of a girl who, appearances to the contrary notwithstanding, wanted very much to marry and settle down. Heard door bell and opened door to Afonso, forgetting hair in curlers. Took him into the drawing room, caught sight of myself in mirror and asked why he hadn't told me; he said it gave him a nice feeling of being married to me. At this I burst into tears. Bit Afonso's head off in the middle of his sentence about long engagements and retired to take hair out of curlers. Came back looking and feeling better and told him about the row with Philippa; I said the actual row not important, but dismal fact was that from the moment of our sharing the flat, we'd seemed to drift in different directions; lifelong association now seemed to count for nothing. Afonso said this not unusual, as many childhood associations more from habit than from choice. He said he was glad I wasn't like Philippa, and that I had saved myself up for him. I told him, slowly and with emphasis, that I had not, repeat not, saved myself up for anybody, least of all him; if he was interested in my moral attitude, such as it was, I had no specific objection to a girl sleeping with the man she loved if something was holding up the wedding—money, for example—but that in every case I knew of, which included most of my old school friends, the man became a series of men, and getting into bed became a routine performance. I said that what frightened me was the word promiscuous. Afonso asked if I would go out and have a promiscuous dinner with him; looked it up in dictionary and found it meant mixture without order or distinction. Felt glad, as went out and shut door of flat, that I wasn't going to be there much longer.

Thursday May 4th.

Bought sandwiches and ate them in office for lunch and began belated study of Portuguese, page 1 lesson 1.

After office, went with Afonso to see his parish priest and have a Little Talk, also to sign paper promising to allow children to be Catholics. Learned on the way there that Afonso had already had to sign a paper stating why he wanted to marry a non-Catholic. I asked what reasons he'd given; he said they must have been good ones, as he'd got permission. I said that was Jolly Decent of the Pope. Signed paper, Afonso withdrew to allow me to talk to the priest, priest nice little man but seemed to me to have too-ready patter, so found Little Talk petering out on my side; very glad to see Afonso reappear. On way home, tried out my Portuguese on him; he said it was very good Spanish.

Friday May 5th.

Left office with, surprisingly, regret. Boss curt to end, but junior typists filed into room with wedding present: fruit bowl. Office boy presented own gift: ash tray marked, touchingly, A Present From London. Liftman made speech: no other young lady so pleasant, and so on and so on; all this listened to without enthusiasm by several people waiting to take the lift up again. Walked into rain feeling depressed; Afonso waiting outside in car. Hadn't expected him, but he said he was there to mop me up, as though leaving office not unduly moving, present state of my nerves seemed to necessitate somebody constantly at hand with supply of handkerchiefs. Drove straight out to dine at the Four-in-Hand at Roehampton; nice place, wonderful food, soothing wine. Drove home feeling much refreshed, only to be brought down to earth by Afonso's remark that there were now only two hundred and twenty-two shopping days before Christmas—in other words, only four days before his parents arrived. He said they were bringing his brothers and sisters and I asked how many, and he said all of them. I said The Lot? and he said all except Duarte, who in Brazil. Felt suddenly panic-stricken and insisted on reciting their names and ages until I'd got them right. Couldn't sleep. Tried counting sheep, but found myself counting José, Vasco, Duarte, Alberto, Maria, Ana, Valeria, Francisco and Luiz. They weren't jumping over stiles; I was. And somewhere on the other side, terrifyingly indistinct, was Afonso.

Saturday May 6th.

Had party, which turned out to be two more or less separate parties: (a) English group made up of my relations and *(b)* foreign group, Afonso's friends and mine. Uncle George made good entrance; quite clear that other relations were taking their cue from him, and as he elected to be polite but somewhat distant, they were polite but somewhat distant too. Presented Afonso and felt his speech, his manners and bearing all impeccable, but didn't expect Uncle George to be visibly impressed. Left them together to make what they could of one another, and looked round at all my other relations and thought the whole set of them smug, self-satisfied, ill-informed and uninteresting, especially Uncle George's daughters and their husbands, brought here especially to show me what I could and should have married. Wondered if my family reputation for intellectual conceit, if not snobbery, justified. Uncle George came up to me and said I should have told him that Afonso had spent two years at an English public school, spoke excellent English and could, at a push, be taken for an Englishman. I said that I hadn't mentioned Downside because it was a Catholic school, that Afonso spoke equally good French, German and Spanish and that I didn't really think he would like to be taken, even at a push, for an Englishman. Mother, seeing expression on Uncle George's face, came up to pour oil, but waters too troubled to have much effect. I prayed for everybody but Afonso to go away; prayer answered about 8.15, but not fully, as Mother refused Uncle George's offer of dinner, and stayed to help clear up and wash the glasses. Afonso took her and self out to dinner and then drove her to Waterloo and put her on the 11.5. On way back to flat, I began to howl. Afonso stopped car at Albert Gate and tried to calm me down, but found it hard; immediate future looked to me grim to a degree: meetings with parents, meetings with brothers and sisters, endless details to remember about wedding arrangements; leaving Mother, leaving dogs, leaving home. Afonso said would I remember that he loved me and would always love me; at this, howled more than ever. I wondered if I could be growing like Mother's youngest sister Blanche, who was reported to have snuffled from cradle to grave, which appropriately enough was watery one. Afonso reminded me of how we'd fallen in love; not at once, but slowly; slowly and thoroughly. I said that it did rather look as though we were meant to get together; if he hadn't come to England to buy horses and if I hadn't gone to that point-to-point and bumped into him coming out of the sandwich bar, who knows? Felt better, and said I thought relations meant very little one way or the other, as one had to leave them and cleave unto one's husband. Afonso said all relations really alike; his own busy wondering why he couldn't have married a nice Portuguese girl, but would stop wondering as soon as they set eyes on me. At this, I cried because I loved him so much. He said his handkerchief now useless, so drove me home and drove away.

Sunday May 7th.

Went to Holy Communion at Westminster Abbey and wondered how long it would be before I could attend another service there; soaked in as much atmosphere as possible. Afonso came to the flat after Mass; I finished my packing, tidied the rooms, said a brief, glad farewell to the landlady, left the key in paper shop down the road and drove to cottage with Afonso, lunching on way at riverside restaurant. Afonso stayed to supper and then went away. Mother came into my room to say goodnight, and told me she was very glad I was going to have these last weeks with her at home. I gave her a brief and expurgated account of the row with Philippa, and added that Philippa had been under the impression that some of the rumours spread by her. Mother very upset, asked me in horror if I thought so too. Said no. She said she had had her suspicions for some time, but had said nothing to anybody, least of all Philippa's parents. She went on to say that she hoped she was mistaken, but she did wonder whether Philippa hadn't allowed freedom to go to her head. I said nothing. Mother sat brooding on my bed for a while and said that one read, one heard, one even saw on Television evidence that young people's morals not what they were. I looked at her and asked with genuine curiosity: "What exactly *were* they?" She said: "You mean in my day?" and I said yes. She thought it over for a time, and then said that of course there had always been girls ready to kick over the traces, but in her day they were in the minority. I said well, in *my* day *(a)* no traces to kick and *(b)* I myself, taking a cross-section of old class mates, with obvious exception of Clara Cornhill, was in a minority of one. Mother unable to say anything for a time, and finally said couldn't and wouldn't believe it. This seemed to me beside the point, so I said nothing. After a pause, Mother asked in broken tones what, in that case, had marriage become? I said I thought that the general idea between married couples nowadays was that least asked, soonest answered. Long silence, out of which Mother thanked God out loud and with obvious sincerity that I had had the strength to resist temptation. Said I was sorry to interrupt her devotions, but my resistance had not been to temptation, but to oversexed young men in search of inexpensive outlets. Mother, after studying me closely, said that there was a lot of great-aunt Sophie in me. I didn't care to follow this up.

Monday May 8th.

Uncle George and Aunt Freda to lunch to improve acquaintance with Afonso. Afonso and I in garden when they arrived; Afonso anxious to be friendly, but Uncle George's greeting so far from cordial that Afonso withdrew into shell. He kissed Aunt Freda's hand; she, being less accustomed to this form of greeting than Mother now is, looked somewhat startled. Uncle George kissed me on forehead and gave Afonso a brief handshake; Afonso bowed. Party proceeded indoors to join Mother in drawing room.

Uncle George, refusing proffered chair, stood in middle of room and said to Afonso that he was glad of this opportunity of getting to know him better. Afonso bowed. Uncle George said that as the Head of the Family, he was naturally anxious to become well acquainted with niece's fiancé. Afonso bowed. Uncle George said he understood that Afonso's family arriving shortly; he would be happy to meet them. Afonso bowed. Aunt Freda, from sofa, asked him if he had any brothers or sisters. Afonso said yes, he had nine. None? What a pity. *Nine. Nine? Nine?* NINE? Yes, six brothers and three sisters, and he was happy to say that eight were coming over to England with his father and mother. Aunt Freda, shattered, retired from conversation; Uncle George obviously doing mental arithmetic and reaching conclusion that nine and one made ten. Mother said perhaps we could all sit down and have some sherry. Afonso about to bow, but got kick on shin from me, and winced instead. I took him with me to get drinks from the dining room and told him that if he wanted to be funny, I would rather he wasn't funny with Uncle George. Afonso remarked thoughtfully that no race on earth so skilled at veiled insult as the English. I said that Uncle George might be difficult, but from what he, Afonso, had told me, there were one or two relations on his side who couldn't be really chalked up on the credit side, like his half-cracked aunt at Estoril, who played Bridge every day from 3 p.m. to 3.30 a.m. and the completely cracked aunt in Lisbon who thought she was the Empress Joséphine. Afonso said that there was a great difference in not being able to help it, like his aunts, and doing it deliberately, like Uncle George. Took tray of drinks into drawing room and found Uncle George more relaxed, as though he was conscious of having heard The Worst. At lunch, to the surprise of all, he talked non-stop, displaying not to say parading unsuspected knowledge of Manueline architecture, the University of Coimbra, the history of the Port trade, the battle of Aljubarrota and Henry the Navigator. Over coffee in the drawing room, Afonso gave rapid and informed monologue on Stonehenge, London traffic problem, British Army and Navy Campaign medals (with ribbons), the Commonwealth and *The Times* v.

Manchester Guardian. At conclusion of this, Uncle George rose and scooped up Aunt Freda and said they must go now, and quite suddenly brought out biggest family guns, turning before our eyes into General the Hon. George Amyas Leonard St. Quentin Fitzroy (with alphabetical addenda) and announcing with impressive dignity that as Head of Family he would be glad to meet any or all of Afonso's kinsmen— inference quite clear to all: Mother only impecunious widow living in small cottage in country, but behind her full panoply of England's finest if not first family. Afonso bowed, for the first time with respect. Aunt Freda quite pink with what I took to be pride, until Mother explained later that it was panic at the thought of having any or all of Afonso's kinsmen parked on her, her staff consisting of butler (76), cook (74) and house-parlour-kitchen-stillroom-between-maid (**70**).

After supper, discussed honeymoon plans with Afonso; got nowhere, and had disagreement over the question of where and when I should meet his parents. He said at the airport; I said no, I'd get lost among the crowd of brothers and sisters, and it would be far better to wait and go with him to see them at their hotel when they were settled in. Afonso drove away saying he considered this a great mistake.

Tuesday May 9th.

Discovered for myself that it was a great mistake when summoned to dine at Claridges, where entire family staying. Wore my new green; part of trousseau, but felt it would give me much-needed confidence. Afonso came down to the cottage and drove me up to London, much more subdued than I'd ever seen him, from which I deduced that he, too, was encountering family difficulties. Disembarking at hotel, I felt suddenly that at this first meeting, Mother should have been present. Afonso said no; Mother not marrying him, only me. Only me found confidence rapidly oozing on way up in lift. Ushered by Afonso into elegant suite, drawing room of which appeared to be crammed with people. Unnerving hush on my entrance; populace fell back, leaving lane up to Afonso's mother and father. Father tall, dark, wearing glasses; Mother short, stoutish; one of those women one sees in smart gatherings in France and Spain—sleek black hair, close-fitting, beautifully-cut (usually) black dress, diamonds gleaming everywhere, small hands and pretty feet in five-inch heels, flawless make-up and complete poise. She spoke in good English but—unlike Afonso—with a foreign accent. She took my hand and for the next few minutes or hours I toured the family, beginning with Afonso's father. When members of family finished with, started on the hangers-on: thin and sinister-looking family priest; severe-looking, black-clad companion or duenna; cousins and uncles and aunts dug up from various business or Ambassadorial posts to take a look at me and see what Afonso had let himself in for. My impressions more and more confused, but one thing beginning to emerge very clearly indeed: that I was in the centre of a gold-plated circle, and that it was possible if not probable that I was expected to produce something pretty solid in return. I thought of the cottage, with its little garden, its six-acre paddock and two-acre orchard. I thought of our sturdy but aged horse and our far-from-sturdy aged car. I thought that anybody who was looking for solid returns would be pretty disappointed. Asked Afonso (on way to Aunt Edwina's, in Wimpole Street, where I was spending the night) how rich he was; he said he wasn't, but his parents were; by Portuguese law, every child inherits equally, so must divide unknown sum by ten. I said was he entirely dependent on his parents, and he said more or less, but that he worked for his father and got small wage plus free house, food and fuel; salary not yet adjusted to married state, but Papa would take care of everything. I said this from an Englishman would have sounded highest degree of cadging. Afonso said yes, he realised that, but conditions quite different in Portugal; he himself of independent turn of mind but considered himself his father's right-hand man and therefore worthy of his hire, and I would have to learn to think in new terms. Said I'd I try. He said his parents very pleased with me. I said that on the whole very pleased with his parents, but too early to commit myself.

Couldn't sleep, so spent half the night sorting out brothers and sisters as follows:

Name	Age	Characteristics
José	28	Smallish, thin, attractive, shy smile; has something to do with Portuguese Navy.

Vasco	26	With name like that, ought to have some thing to do with Portuguese Navy, but manages one of his father's estates, like Afonso only on smaller scale. Is handsome, with roving eye.
Duarte	25	Manages father's estate in Brazil.
Alberto	24	Large black mournful eyes; doing some thing at Coimbra University; studious type.
Maria	22	Engaged, fiancé at hotel but can't recall him; will look like her mother in time but at present fresh and glowing. Talks a lot in several languages.
Ana	20	The beauty of the family; dark, a bit wistful but quite alluring.
Valeria	18	Small, thin, pretty figure, gay and giggly. The sexy one.
Francisco	16	
Luiz	14	Might be twins; both obviously adore Alfonso

N.B. All well-turned-out and all waited on hand and foot; all good-mannered. Girls apparently in the charge of black-clad duenna.

Wednesday May 10th.

Afonso drove me down to the cottage; told me impression made on his family extremely favourable. He stayed to lunch and tea and we sat in the garden and discussed honeymoon plans, but couldn't decide between the Lakes, the Highlands, the Bahamas, the Greek Islands, the Dales and the Dolomites. He left about six, and Uncle George and Aunt Freda drove over for supper. Uncle George, over coffee, stated his intention of calling on Afonso's family at Claridge's, telling them who he was and inviting them to a small dinner party with himself and Aunt Freda and Mother and Afonso and myself. Mother very upset at this suggestion, said quite out of the question; she had, she said, already written to Afonso's mother asking her and her husband to lunch at the cottage tomorrow, 11th. Long and tense pause, at the end of which she added that Uncle George and Aunt Freda could come too, if they liked. Uncle George said in angry tone that yes, they did like; they liked very much, and if Mother couldn't see that having no husband, she needed the support of the Head of the Family, he would like to point the fact out to her; added that he had been making enquiries, and although he stood by what he had said about the unwisdom of marrying into a foreign country and a foreign religion, he was glad to learn that the family had some Standing. Mother said in cold tone that all necessary enquiries had been made by her before permitting the match; she had not concerned herself with Standing, but had assured herself of Afonso's high moral character, love of his parents and family, general devotion to duty and particular devotion to me. Uncle George said all very well, but my family owed it to me to put down card for card; they were an old family, but we were older; they might have more money but we undoubtedly had more social weight and it was his duty to let them feel it. Mother said she was sorry to seem ungrateful, but she felt strongly that Afonso and Afonso's family were lucky to get me, and she was certain they felt the same, and social weight didn't enter into it. Uncle George said no use trying to make women see sense, and added that he and Aunt Freda would be here at one fifteen sharp.

Thursday May 11th.

Completely successful lunch. Heavenly day; sun pouring down on cottage, roses a-bloom, muslin curtains fluttering, dogs on lawn, lawn mowed by postman evening before, general effect very picture-postcard. Only flaw slight smell which got worse; traced to cesspool, which was found to need emptying. Too late for action; postman sent for, not available, but postmistress came round with supply of disinfectant; several buckets of this diluted in water and poured round offending area, and earth shovelled over by self and Mother. No other contretemps. Afonso came early; his parents came later in imposing hired Daimler, driving in just behind Uncle George's twenty-four-year-old-Rolls-good-as-the-day-I-bought-it-my-dear-feller. Introductions, bowing and hand-shaking. Uncle George and Afonso's father instantly found common ground, each being convinced bestowing great honour in allowing match. Afonso's mother in bronze-and-white silk suit; Mother in tweed suit; utterly dissimilar in every way, but united in exchanging quite genuine compliments about son and daughter; quite clear that Mother loved Afonso dearly and had no doubt his mother was going to love me equally. Settled, after discussion, that I was to call Afonso's parents Mama and Papa. Went into lunch; fresh asparagus; chicken from neighbouring farm, mushrooms from paddock, peas from garden, frozen strawberries, cream from postman's cow, coffee from Portugal, donated by Afonso. Mother had look of quiet satisfaction, as if certain that Claridge's couldn't have done better. After lunch, Uncle George took Afonso and Papa to watch village cricket practice; ladies sat in chairs on lawn. Men came back to tea; Mother took Mama to see Church but couldn't get in, as locked and key unavailable. I asked Mama if Maria and Ana would be bridesmaids; she said they would of course be delighted. Aunt Freda offered me family bridal veil, I said thank you, but too much responsibility, and had bought one.

Drove up to the airport with Afonso at 6, to meet Inez and her brother, and Antoinette. Very gay meeting; everybody delighted with everybody else. We had drinks in the bar and I began to feel for the first time that getting married could be quite a party—and then I saw Clara Cornhill standing outside with her father, both looking unutterably dreary as usual. Tried to keep my mind off them, but found myself contrasting our group with those two, and wondering what it felt like to be Clara Cornhill and wanted by nobody. Passed her on the way out; would have liked to go on, but her father quite determined to meet Afonso. Stopped and performed introductions and then went on and then quite suddenly took leave of my senses, asked the others to wait for me, turned and went back and asked Clara Cornhill if she'd be one of my bridesmaids. Understood from her garbled outpourings that she would, went back to the others and drove back with them to town. Afonso put me on the train after dinner; got home at 10 and heard from ticket collector that Philippa had come on the train before. Thought of phoning her when I got home, decided not to. Later, saw her walking up the drive. Opened the door; she came in and said she was home for good, having given up her job but not the flat, as she was going to get married. I said I wished her and Francis luck, and she said Oh, no, not Francis, she was going to marry Charles Staple. I asked who Charles Staple was, and she said didn't I remember, he used to come to the flat sometimes; he had a yellow sports car. I said I had no idea she liked him, and she said that after Francis, she could like anybody; added that she thought men, with few exceptions, double-crossers, out for what they could get and far too selfish to give anything in return for what they took, and Francis and the rest of them could go and boil themselves for all she cared, and if I hadn't fixed up definitely about bridesmaids, she'd like to be one after all. Walked to gate with her, went back and told Mother that Philippa engaged to man with yellow sports car, forgot to mention bridesmaid detail.

Friday May 12th.

Went to lunch, with Mother, at Lusitania Club in Hanover Square, at Mama's invitation. Got there a few minutes too early, but it was worth it to see royal reception accorded to Mama on her arrival. Mother said she was sorry the girls weren't with Mama; Mama said they were with Papa at National Gallery; she said much better for us three to meet alone in order to settle a few points.

Point 1. Bridesmaids. Ana and Maria delighted and would like to meet the other two bridesmaids. I said now not two others but four others; Mother very surprised at this but I explained that in telling her about Philippa had forgotten to add that she was going to be a bridesmaid after all.

Mother said who was the other one? I said Clara Cornhill, and said I'd asked her at the airport. Mother said: "Oh, *what* a good thing, I *knew* you'd bring yourself to do it in the end, poor, poor little Clara." Mama looked surprised and somewhat apprehensive at this, but nobody bothered to explain. Mama said wasn't six rather a large number for so small a Church and I said yes.

Point 2. Officiating priest. Mama said that family priest, with special permission, would perform ceremony, assisted by local priest. Luiz to act as server. Explained to Mother that this Afonso's youngest brother.

Point 3. This was raised by Mother, who asked Mama who was going to arrange the music for the Service. Mama looked surprised and said Music? No music. Mother, in astounded voice, said What, no music? and Mama said No, no music; she went on to explain that the Service for a mixed marriage was very brief indeed; a mere half-hour, as no Nuptial Mass possible in circumstances; therefore no music. Mother said but why not? Mama said that mixed Service very brief, Nuptial Mass not possible in circumstances, therefore no music. Mother said yes, she understood about the Nuptial Mass the first time Mama said it, but why no music even so? Mama said that Service for mixed marriage printed on card and read out in Latin and English and that was all, and no place and no arrangements for any music, as of course not possible to have non-Catholic music. No comment from Mother, but I knew that she was feeling upset, as she studied the organ and plays it wonderfully. My own feeling was that two priests reading off a card, and no music, wasn't exactly the wedding I'd dreamed about. Felt depressed, ordered steak, heard Mama ask for the fish menu and remembered that this was Friday; Mama ordered sole. Mother said in firm voice that she would have steak like me; from her expression, I deduced that she was losing her Leanings, owing to family priests and no music.

Drove back to cottage; Mother silent but came out of reverie to ask me what became of that music teacher at my school, the one who left on becoming a Catholic? I said I didn't know, but I thought that Aunt Freda had mentioned her recently, as ex-teacher had relations in Aunt Freda's village and went to visit them now and then. Mother asked me to stop at grocer's; I said what did she want to buy, to which Mother replied that he was a Catholic. Went in; Mother asked grocer if any Choir formed for new Church; grocer said funny she should ask that, he'd been scratching up all the singers in the district who were also Catholics, and had just succeeded in forming what he'd call a nucleus, if we knew what he meant. Mother said she was so interested, and when did they practise? He said at odd moments in evening, but Saturday evenings best for all, and usually good attendance; he asked Mother to come and hear them and Mother said she would love to.

Got home; Mother phoned Aunt Freda; said when next ex-music-teacher visiting relations in village, would Aunt Freda inform by telephone; very important, would explain later, but no need to mention it to Uncle George.

Saturday May 13th.

Went to town to attend Bridesmaids' Lunch, held at Mother's Club, as considered more sheltered for Afonso's sisters. They arrived with black-clad duenna in tow; Philippa's reaction one of horror, as she thought it was Afonso's mother. Inez came with Antoinette; Antoinette said confidentially that brother of Inez madly in love with her (Antoinette) and so she was enjoying this visit to England even more than she had expected to. Saw Clara Cornhill coming in and noted with apprehension that her mother with her; decided to take bull by horns, so went up and said how do you do, Lady Cornhill, so sorry you can't stop, nice of you to bring Clara. She said she was a member of this Club, and I said Oh how nice, and that in that case she could get lunch downstairs. She then said that Clara must on no account be led into any flights of extravagance over bridesmaid's dress.

I said politely that dresses would be kept down to reasonable figure but if Lady Cornhill worried, not too late for Clara to withdraw. Lady Cornhill eyed group with extremely elegant Maria, Ana, Inez and Antoinette and evidently decided wedding worth coming to; said she would leave the matter in my hands, and withdrew. Philippa took Clara aside and said that nobody could help their parents, but if Clara didn't get herself out of their reach soon, her chances of getting anywhere, let alone any men, nil; told her that pink blouse of that shade unsuitable for complexion of that shade, and that after lunch she would take her to Elizabeth Arden's and stand over her while they gave her a complete go-over; after that she would take her to Susan Small's and see that she bought a couple of dresses more suited to present century. Clara said had brought no money and didn't want to buy anything anyway; Philippa said she could put everything down to parents' account. Clara too apprehensive after this to eat much lunch; this not much loss, as Mother's Club not noted for cuisine. Sat on afterwards and decided material, colour and design of dresses and form of accessories. Final choice full, short dresses, pale primrose in order to suit both dark and fair; flat dark green leaves round hair. Party dispersed, Maria and Ana and duenna in tow—familiar Daimler. Philippa carried off Clara. Inez and Antoinette went in search of brother, now necessary to them both.

Drove home to find Afonso there; he had missed me at Club. Had tea with Mother in garden, listened to her suggestions (geographical) for honeymoon, made no decision. Afonso couldn't stay to supper; hardly had Mother and I finished ours when Uncle George and Aunt Freda drove up to (they said) talk about the wedding. Found that wedding arrangements passing rapidly out of my hands into informal Committee consisting of Uncle George (Chairman), Aunt Freda and Aunt Mary (Vice) and several other aunts and uncles and cousins. Uncle George said of course we would have the reception at his house and I said of course we wouldn't; reception was going to be here at the cottage, and nowhere else. Uncle George said out of the question, as couldn't fit more than a dozen guests into pocket-handkerchief of a garden. I said not in garden; marquee in paddock adjoining garden. Uncle George wanted to know why pay (and *who* pay?) large sum for marquee when not at all necessary. I explained that I had already asked our postman, owner of the marquee put up on village green for cricket matches; he had said that he would gladly lend it if I'd pay the men for putting up and taking it down again. Uncle George said couldn't possibly use that tattered, leaky old tent; when he played in Visitors' team last summer, rain poured in through innumerable rents. I said leaks or not, was going to have my wedding reception in my own home. Argument followed, in middle of which I burst into tears, first time in front of Uncle George since early childhood. He look Mother aside and recommended intensive course of *Sanatogen.* He and Aunt Freda went away. Phone rang; Philippa, speaking from main line station, said would I ask my mother to ring up Lady Cornhill and tell her that Clara was staying with me for the night. I said Clara wasn't; Philippa said yes, she was; she was bringing her down and would be at our house in about half an hour. I asked why Clara couldn't go home to her own house; Philippa said this quite impossible owing to dyed hair. I said why couldn't Clara stay at Philippa's house and Philippa said no, Lady Cornhill only reassured if my mother rang up. She said that sorry to be so late, but had to give Clara dinner in the flat to Bolster her up. I reported this conversation to Mother; she said she always knew Philippa had some good in her, and how kind to take poor Clara in hand; somebody should have done it long ago. Told me to make up spare bed while she rang up Lady Cornhill.

Philippa arrived with Clara at 10.30. Clara completely unrecognisable and living proof that Art frequently triumphant over Nature. Hair pale gold, make-up pale peach; figure in cunning dress no longer lanky but willowy. Mother and I, genuinely impressed, told Philippa that she had done a good job. Philippa, gratified, went home; Clara divided between pleasure and panic; Mother gave her an aspirin and sent her up to bed.

Sunday May 14th.

Difficult day. Clara sent over to Philippa's to be out of the way when her mother came to fetch her. On the arrival of

Lady Cornhill, Mother met her and led her into drawing room and closed the door. Hung about, but heard nothing more than steady buzz. Went to prepare lunch, heard car driving away and came out to ask Mother what had happened. She said she had been frank with Lady Cornhill (didn't say what about) and had urged her to allow Clara to join Philippa in flat until Philippa's marriage to Mr. Staple, who turns out to be Lady Cornhill's great-nephew, which in some way seems to ensure that Philippa entirely suitable chaperon for Clara. Lady Cornhill had gone away to talk her husband into agreeing to this plan.

Lunch no sooner over than visit from Francis Welby. Walked round and round lawn; he said Philippa was out of her mind; refused to see him and had written some tommy-rot about marrying a guy called Staple, a cad if ever there was one, and certain to lead her a dog's life, if not worse. I said I hadn't pleasure of Mr. Staple's acquaintance, but considered Philippa old enough to know what she was doing. Francis said he knew quite well what she was doing: she was trying to get him, Francis Welby, to marry her. Failing him, any cad with a yellow sports car would do. I said in that case how fortunate Mr. Staple handy, and would Francis go away now, as I was busy. He asked if I meant to stand there and tell him I wouldn't go and talk to Philippa. I asked what about, and he said about himself, naturally. I said I was sorry, but that I had had the opportunity of studying his friendship with Philippa at close quarters, and it had seemed to me that Philippa was doing what he and I were doing now: going round in circles and getting nowhere. Left him on lawn; looked out of window of hall and saw him walking away.

Mother went to tea with Philippa's mother. I went into kitchen to start on special Portuguese supper for Afonso. Heard him coming and called to him and he came into the kitchen and asked what the peculiar smell was, and I said his supper: dried salt cod obtained at great trouble on my behalf and at my expense by Philippa from shop in Soho. Afonso suggested sending it back to shop, as dried salt cod not really his favourite dish. I said this had nothing to do with it; I was doing it as a nice surprise for him. He said perhaps surprise, but not nice. I asked him exactly what part of Portugal we were going to live in, and he said he had told me not once, but four hundred times: in the Ribatejo.

I said yes, I'd heard that, but where exactly was it? He said if I gave him a map of Portugal, he'd show me. I said no map of Portugal. He said atlas would do. Abandoned cod, looked for atlas, failed to find. Found article on Portugal in encyclopedia, but Afonso said map totally inadequate; if I would give him some paper, he would draw a map for me. Found paper; Afonso spread it on kitchen table and proceeded to draw map of Portugal. Halfway through, he remembered he had one in his car and went to fetch it. He spread it on floor of drawing room and proceeded to point out provinces of Portugal. I said no need for geography lesson; I had simply asked where the Ribatejo was; all he had to do was to put his finger on it, and let me go back to my cod. He said essential, he would have said, for a girl marrying a Portuguese to know the elements of the country's geography. I said I would take a special course in it at some other time, but for the present would he kindly merely swiftly and above all briefly indicate where the beastly Ribatejo was. He said if I would only look, I would see: Here was Lisbon and here was the Tagus or Tejo; I could follow its course. I said had not the faintest intention of following its course, and said if he asked me, I'd say he didn't know where the Ribatejo was and was just covering up while he tried to find it. He said, in slow and measured tones, that the Ribatejo was between the Alto Alentejo and Estremadura. I said that information would only interest those who knew where the Alto Alentejo and Estremadura were, and added that I had often heard about the man who, asked what the time was, proceeded to take the clock to pieces, but this was the first time I had really seen the process demonstrated, and heaven help our children if they ever went to him and asked a simple, easy question and expected to get a simple, easy answer. Afonso said did I or did I not want to know where the Ribatejo was. I said I didn't want to know where it was, didn't care where it was, didn't care what it was between. Mother came in and said did I know something in the kitchen was burnt to ashes? Wish I knew if Afonso did it purposely.

Tuesday May 16th.

Maria, Ana and Valeria came down to lunch at the cottage. Arrived in same old Daimler, with female duenna, chaperon or companion, still draped in heavy black. Mother told me to lay extra place. Girls enjoyed every minute, especially helping in kitchen before and after lunch, but only too obvious none of them, like Afonso, had ever done hand's turn before. Mother not too enchanted by their frequent delighted reference to "tiny little doll's house". Took them, at duenna's request, to see the Church; key now left by priest in village for use when required.

Wednesday May 17th.

Letter from Aunt Mary: It didn't seem worth while buying anything expensive just for one occasion, so could Mother lend her, for wedding, that little fur tippet she (Aunt Mary) had given her on her twenty-first birthday? She would return it immediately after the wedding.

Aunt Freda rang up: ex-music-teacher coming next day. Mother said would Aunt Freda please invite teacher to tea, and also invite us. Aunt Freda said yes if she must, but why? Mother said would explain later.

Thursday May 18th.

Went to tea with Aunt Freda and music mistress. Music mistress obviously surprised at sudden accession of friendliness, as relations between us at school not cordial. Mother said how nice to see her again, and was hoping she would help her: New Catholic Church in our village, newly-formed Choir but nobody to train them; did music mistress ever have an evening to spare and if so, could she possibly spare it and help the Choir to get going? Music mistress very co-operative, said she could spare two Wednesday evenings before going to stay with relations in Ireland. On way home, I asked Mother what she had in mind, and she said music for the wedding, what else?

Friday May 19th.

Rung up by Mama and asked if I would like to meet her in town and go shopping. Said yes; she said meet her at Quaglino's for lunch. After lunch climbed into Daimler but found shops not what I call shops; expensive establishments right out of my shopping class. Sat in couturier's salon watching the models glide by; recognised one with surprise as old school buddy Etta Hargreaves. Thought Mama was shopping for herself until she stopped Etta (now, I learned, called Miss Echo) and said she thought that one would suit me. I said, when could speak, that thank you, but something simpler (meaning one-twentieth of probable price) far better for me. No notice taken of this; was conducted to elegant fitting room and found myself staring into long glass at gorgeous creature gorgeously attired. Etta (Echo) came in wearing yet another creation; this also bought for me. Didn't see any money passing hands, so no opportunity to see how much; spent rest of the afternoon worrying about how many starving families could have lived for how long on unknown though surely enormous amount.

Inherit this wet-blanket trait from Mother, as from all accounts my father never did sums concerning starving families, being convinced that he would always have enough money and that he would live for ever. He hadn't, and he didn't; his sole legacy to Mother feeling of financial insecurity—and of course, myself.

Saturday May 20th.

Afonso came down, and we drove to Brighton to keep date with Great-aunt Lorna. Found her mansion on sea front more mouldering than ever. Door opened by mouldering butler; led through rooms with shrouded furniture and into drawing room where Great-aunt Lorna, more aged but as imposing as ever, talked as usual non-stop. Sherry before lunch, but rather ominous lecture from Aunt Lorna on danger of eating heavy meals in the middle of the day; went into lunch to discover nothing more than small slice of melon, small helping of fish soufflé and smaller helping of strawberry mousse. Afonso looked anxiously for cheese to fill up, but none; fruit brought to table but after one peach each, removed again. Aunt Lorna sent us out for a walk while she rested; went to a sandwich bar and had coffee and ham sandwiches. Went back to tea; so far no mention of wedding present which original reason for coming to lunch; hoped Aunt Lorna hadn't forgotten. Caraway-seed cake for tea, after which Aunt Lorna said she had been looking through her things and had laid out some of them; would we choose one as wedding present? Led into library; dust sheets on all furniture except marble-topped table on which things laid out as follows: (1) enormous Georgian silver soup ladle (2) very small tortoise-shell snuff box (3) set of old *Encyclopaedia Britannica* (4) old family album with family photographs 1880-1897 (5) crystal decanter, top unfortunately missing (6) scent bottle with silver band engraved P.L. (previous but unknown owner). Stood with Afonso looking at the things; felt depressed, not because I was disappointed in them but because I knew the house was full of lovely and valuable things which Aunt Loma was clearly determined to take with her. Afonso examined objects with reverence, said that choice was of course mine, but he himself would very much like the family album. I said I would too. Aunt Lorna, very pleased, covered everything else up with dust sheets in case we changed our minds. Spent rest of visit looking through album. Drove home with it wrapped in silk scarf on seat between us. I said I hoped he didn't think gift too grudging, as Aunt Lorna, like Aunt Mary, very thrifty not to say miserly. Afonso said that anybody who gave a thing away at such sacrifice was making a more generous gesture than somebody who, having less feeling of possession, gave away more. I said I loved him very much. He said he loved me too, but what on earth was that cake we had at tea-time, with things that were still sticking in between his teeth? I explained old English tea-time custom of caraway-seed cake.

Monday May 22nd.

Letter from Aunt Mary: she hadn't been able to find anything nice in the shops by way of a wedding present; had decided to send a cheque. No cheque enclosed.

Francis Welby appeared at 6.30. Walked round lawn until dogs giddy. He said all women were treacherous, Philippa more than most. I said natural for girls to want to marry and settle down. He said marry on what? He had £15 in the Bank and didn't like his job (also in Bank) and thought of starting out on his own; didn't say where to. Asked me to point out to Philippa that marriage impossible in these circumstances. I asked him why he didn't go into his father's extremely flourishing firm; he said father and firm both anathema. I said in this case why not let Philippa settle down with somebody else ? He said he could see he was wasting his time. I said he was wasting mine too. Parted with relief on both sides.

Tuesday May 23rd

Up to town to see bridesmaids trying on their dresses. Thought they all looked very nice, even Clara newly-glamorous Cornhill, but felt that they were going to more than fill the aisle as they came up it. All went on to Claridge's for lunch at invitation of Mama. After lunch, Mama took me aside to say that she and Papa would like to pay for our honeymoon. Thanked her, but said although very grateful I felt we could manage it ourselves, as Afonso had shown me a letter from a Brazilian uncle of his called Feliciano, promising to send us a cheque which he hoped we would use for travel. Mama said that Uncle Feliciano very good man, very pious, very kind, very sweet, but very old and very forgetful. On way back to cottage with Afonso told him of Mama's offer; he said pity I turned it down, as though Uncle Feliciano very good man, very pious, very kind, very sweet, was also very old and very forgetful; sometimes he forgot to send the cheque and sometimes he sent the cheque but forgot to have money in Bank to meet it. I said in this case why not wash out Uncle Feliciano and pay for our honeymoon with other, less chancy, wedding cheques? Afonso said wedding cheques meant for setting up house and not for squandering on honeymoon. I pointed out that the word squander in connection with honeymoon with me not at all appropriate; also that our house already set up. Added that I found it terribly confusing not to know exactly how much we were going to have to live on, and he said of course we knew: his salary, and presents from his uncles and aunts, and money from his father and mother; we would never, never want for anything. He asked if I would rather he went to and from the City every day and handed over his weekly wage in an envelope every Friday, and I said in a way, yes; one would then know where one stood. Promised him I would try to believe that although it didn't look like it to me, he really was absolutely independent. He then handed me small package from his parents, to be opened when he had gone. Opened it when he had gone, found love from Mama and Papa, and brooch in form of rose. Put it on and showed it to Mother; she said very pretty; she had seen one in the costume jewellery department of Harrods, and thought how nice.

Wednesday May 24th.

Music mistress came to supper; afterwards went with her and Mother to the Church, where Choir assembled, eleven strong, total of combined ages probably one thousand. Sopranos shrill, altos shaky. Late-comer entered, making round dozen; he shook Mother cordially by the hand and said didn't she remember, she had accompanied him once during far-off wartime concert when he had sung Speak, Speak, Speak to me Thora. Mother said yes, she did remember. Choir proceeded under baton of music mistress.

Mother went to organ and suddenly Church filled with heavenly sound. Priest came in and listened. At conclusion of practice, he said a pity no music possible at wedding.

Friday May 26th.

Letter from Aunt Mary: could Mother lend her the old black handbag she lent her for the Mayer wedding? Would return it immediately after ceremony. Was sending cheque in next letter.

To dinner at Uncle George's: gala evening of dinner party for Afonso and parents. Wore my brooch and saw Uncle George eyeing it during evening; hoped he hadn't seen it in Harrods' costume jewellery department. To even up numbers and provide partner for Mother, distant cousin Douglas had been located and brought out of retirement; once third or fourth Sea Lord, now well on in years but wearing well. Full resources of house called on; effect impressive; quiet but unmistakably solid. Dinner very good, owing to Mother having spent two previous days helping cook. Wine wonderful, due to hitherto unsuspected supply in Uncle George's cellar. Conversation at dinner like tennis match at Wimbledon, with Uncle George and Afonso serving and returning Stonehenge, history of the Port Trade, London traffic problem and Battle of Aljubarrota. Gentlemen left in dining room, ladies filed into drawing room, where Mother told Mama of interesting and enthusiastic local Choir, so keen to sing at wedding; if no actual ban against purely Catholic music sung by purely Catholic Choir in purely Catholic Church, surely good thing to have music at wedding of young couple? Mama said no actual ban. Mother said she wondered if Mama knew somebody of influence in Church (Catholic) circles who could look into matter and give decision? Mama understood to say knew several influential persons, would look into matter. Visitors left; Mother and I stayed and I thanked Uncle George and Aunt Freda for giving party, which undoubted success. Uncle George said great pleasure, proper thing for him to do, must stand behind his sister and his niece. He then said would like a closer look at brooch; where had it come from? I said from Mama and Papa, and took it off. Uncle George examined it, said By Jove several times and at last handed it Aunt Freda. Mother said she thought it very pretty. Uncle George said pretty or not, he wouldn't care to put a value of less than five hundred pounds on it. Long pause. Mother, in faint voice, said Nonsense. Uncle George said hadn't she realised the thing was valuable? Mother said had no idea; was he sure? Uncle George said of course he was sure; did she think people of that kind would give their eldest son's wife something out of a cracker? Mother said no, of course not, and added that it would be better if she held the brooch on way home, as might be lost. Driving home, talked money with Mother for the first time—that is, for the first time seriously and with an understanding of what it was I wanted to know. Learned that there had never been much. Father heir to Truscombe title through a distant cousin; also heir to Truscombe fortune—but father died before the cousin, and the title and the money passed to the next in succession and Mother put what little money she had into Trust for me, to bring me in small but steady income. Tried to tell her I was grateful for all she'd done; made her promise to come out frequently to Portugal and stay for long periods. She said she would, especially when babies came. Got home and put brooch in safe: i.e. in case, in cardboard box, in paper, in small attaché case hidden on top of Mother's wardrobe.

Saturday May 27th.

Afonso came down for weekend. Packed a picnic lunch and tea, and spent day down by the river; warm and sunny. Discussed honeymoon plans and suddenly found them falling into place: are going to the Canaries, not on expensive liner at Papa's expense, but on a Spanish tomato boat called the *San Miguel,* sailing from London at 6.30 on the day of the wedding. From Canaries, not returning to England, but going straight to Lisbon. I realised for the first time that after the wedding, I would be severing all home ties and going to a strange country to be engulfed by Mama and Papa and José, Vasco, Alberto, Maria, Ana, Valeria, Francisco and Luiz, to say nothing of the priest and the black-clad companion. Told Afonso I understood why brides decamped in panic on eve of wedding. Afonso said he had never heard of a bride decamping; only bridegrooms. I asked him to try to give me some kind of picture of our future life; he said the background was 2000 acres in the Ribatejo; horses all over the place as that was his job; Papa had built up splendid stock, and his horses were becoming renowned, as witness Afonso's recent trip to Paris to sell to famous racehorse owner. Our house: long, low, white, ranch-type, comfortable and adequately staffed but without modem amenities like running hot and cold, gas, electricity and so on, as miles from anywhere; nearest neighbours three miles away; drive to Lisbon took three and a half hours; number of visits to Lisbon to be decided by myself, many or few as I pleased. Headquarters in Lisbon suite of rooms in spreading family mansion with wonderful view of Tagus estuary. Our friends always ready and eager to come up for weekends; the whole family came up for August. Afonso's working day: up at 6, out until 8.30. Back to the house for ample and unhurried breakfast. Out again until 1 unless very hot; back to house for lunch. In house until 4.30 unless very hot; back at 7 and then home for rest of day. In saddle most of working hours. Our staff, loosely speaking: five maids, two men, two cooks, three or four water carriers and odds and ends for poultry and sheep and so on. I said was that all? He said was I quite, quite sure? I said if I hadn't been before, I was now. He said did I realise that we were to be married in exactly one week from now; that in fact at this time next week, I would be married to him; his. Said yes, I did realise. Added, after consideration, that I was very glad.

Tuesday May 30th.

Answers to wedding invitations still pouring in; wedding presents coming in in shoals; postmistress has got her niece in to help. Spend almost all my time knee-deep in wrapping paper or sitting at desk saying thank you. Wedding dress home and hung up.

Am to have music. Phone call from Mama just before lunch: her priest talked to parish priest who talked to local priest who talked to Bishop who said yes. Mother went out and came back with the Form of Service and sat making notes on it and trying over things on the piano, after lunch went out to pay round of calls on members of Choir.

Uncle George's car drew up about 3. I said sorry Mother out; he said good thing, as he really wanted to see me alone, but if it wasn't too early for me to make one, he could do with a cup of tea. Made tea and carried it into garden; Uncle George said pity weather so good now, would be sure to break before wedding. He seemed to be a long time coming round to saying what he'd come round to say, so at last asked him. He said that as a matter of fact he had come in to find out who was giving me away. I stared at him in surprise and said "Why, you of course!" and he said with red face that no Of course about it; this was the kind of thing one expected to be asked to do and this way of taking it for granted was a bit too much. He'd been listening to a lot of talk about bridesmaids and best men and ushers and whatnot, but of who was giving me away, not one word. I said if not him, who else ? he was the only person who could possibly give me away, and I was terribly sorry not to have asked him formally but he knew quite well that nobody else would have done, even if there had been anybody else. He said oh well, now that we'd fixed that up, I needn't expect him to fall flat on his face before the altar like a Mohammedan, because he wouldn't do it. He added that he still thought it a mistake to do what I was doing, but if I had to do it, I couldn't find a better fellow than this Afonso to do it with; pity he insisted on going out to live in Portugal against all advice, but I had a good headpiece and perhaps I'd continue to use it. Promised him I would. Mother came in at this point; I was about to tell her about our having forgotten to ask Uncle George to give me away, when she said to him well, it was about time he had come along, and she did think that the least he could have done was to telephone to ask her how she was coping with everything, and offer to lend a hand, but all he'd done from the very beginning was be obstructive, as usual; carp, carp, carp without ever doing one single thing to take this burden off her shoulders and allow her to have one minute, even one second to enjoy these last days with me, but of course he had always been more ready to lecture than to labour. Here she paused, overcome by tears; Uncle George took me aside, said angrily that of course I had allowed her to overdo it, recommended *Sanatogen.* Mother said she hadn't anticipated all these problems of hotel accommodation, parking, arguments with caterers and so on; too much for one woman, even one woman and daughter. Uncle George said no use talking to women, just so much waste of breath; hadn't he said till he was blue in the face that he was ready to do anything? Hadn't he said it would be too much for her? What was needed was Organisation, and that had never been her strong point.

Uncle George left at 7, barking authoritatively about the A.A. and the R.A.C., London instead of local caterers and special train on morning of wedding, with announcement in *The Times,* this time put in by him. Saw him off and went back to Mother and agreed should have asked him before; can now relax and enjoy the wedding.

Went early to bed, but couldn't sleep; mind full of things past, present and to come. Decided to make myself hot drink, and went to kitchen. Got milk out of fridge and saw face at window; before could panic, recognised Francis Welby. Opened back door and asked him what he thought he was doing, he said he had been walking between this house and Philippa's, desperate; I must help him. Told him to come back in the morning. He said no, would throw himself in river; this so-and-so with yellow car constantly up at flat and his only solace that Clara Cornhill there too and no funny business possible in her presence. He said couldn't understand what had come over Philippa; he hadn't looked at another girl from the moment he first set eyes on her, and this was what he got for it, and if she thought this was the way to drag a man up to the altar, she was very much mistaken. I said he had far better go away and let Philippa marry cad with yellow car if she wanted to; even if unsatisfactory husband, perhaps good father. At this, he sat down on nearest kitchen chair and said he hadn't eaten lunch or dinner and felt weak and could I spare something? Gave him hot milk and cold beef sandwiches, and after another look at him, put some brandy into his milk. Let him out at end of repast and locked door.

Wednesday May 31st.

Letter from Aunt Mary: could someone pick her up, take her to wedding and drop her home again? Public transport unbearable, hire of car unthinkable.

Choir practice, with Choir, music mistress, organist, priest, Mother and self. Music rehearsed for before, during Service and at end of Service. I enter to Regina Coeli; fortunate Uncle George not musical. Ave Maria, sung by professional singer (Catholic) brought along by man who sang

Speak Speak Speak to me Thora; verses of hymns here and there, all very tuneful. Choir much elated at first public appearance, but won't appear as will be up in Choir loft. Home with Mother, who came to my room to say goodnight and said not very long now. Sat on my bed; tears in her eyes but unshed. She said she felt it a terrible responsibility to give her only child over to strangers in a strange country, but had felt from the first that she could trust me fully to Afonso's care and devotion. She asked me if Mama had ever mentioned birth control to me; I said not in so many words, but that she had taken frequent opportunities of saying that God knew what He was doing and would send children as He thought fit. Mother asked if this was Afonso's view too, and I said yes, because he was, first and last and, I hoped, always would be a good Catholic; that was all right with me, and I was quite prepared to wait a few years to see if God really did know what He was doing, but if what He was doing turned out to be a baby a year, I would have to point out that He was overdoing it. Mother's tears began to flow; I took her in embrace and said she wasn't to worry about me. She said she hoped I wouldn't feel too lost without the support of my own Church, and that I would always continue to say my prayers earnestly. I said I would, and that she must come out and check up on me and that she must, must, must come often and stay long. She went away and I rushed to phone and rang up Afonso and felt better after hearing his voice.

Thursday June 1st.

Wedding rehearsal. Long queue of cars outside Church, large crowd inside; everything orderly owing to Uncle George's having held a meeting of ushers and issued strict and detailed instructions which, under his eyes, they were faithfully carrying out. Bridesmaids punctual but long delay owing to disappearance of Vasco and Clara Cornhill; found sitting on river bank. Walked up the aisle on Uncle George's arm while he intoned: One, two, one, two; left, right, don't rush it now, left, right. So intent on this that failed to notice bridegroom waiting at altar. Sank down in genuflection and was surprised and grateful to see Uncle George giving stiff and brief but respectful bow.

Everybody home to tea on lawn; men putting up marquee in paddock; Uncle George went to inspect for holes; no holes but many darns. Had to send out for extra bread and volunteer sandwich-cutters, as ushers unashamedly eating plate after plateful. Aunt Freda said take no notice of Uncle George if he seems upset; he got out his morning suit, and trousers tight in band, have to be let out.

When everybody had left, I walked down to the river with Afonso and we stood for a long, long time, me in his arms, just saying nothing. He said was I happy, and I said yes; only cloud leaving Mother. On return to cottage, Afonso took her in long embrace and made her renew vow of coming out to spend long periods with us. To bed. Slept like log but was awakened by pebbles on window; looked out to see ravaged countenance of

Francis Welby; said he had tried to get into Philippa's house and been thrown out, must see her or would throw himself into river. I said hurry before you change your mind, and shut window. More pebbles; opened window and said if any more of this, would call police. He said did I know Philippa definitely going to marry Staple beast? I said nothing we could do, except mind our own business. Shut window, listened hopefully for splash but heard nothing. Fell asleep, wakened by Mother who said Philippa on phone; went to phone and said would people please remember that people getting married in two days, and Philippa said she was too, but not to yellow car; Francis Welby had just climbed into her mother's bedroom window, shouted at her and waved special licence, demanding hand of daughter. Philippa's father had taken charge; Francis Welby now her fiancé, and asleep in spare bedroom. Said congratulations, went back to bed.

Friday June 2nd.

Nothing. Just Afonso all day, quietly, until he had to go away to his bachelor party.

Saturday June 3rd. s.s. San Miguel.

Married. Wedding in every respect a success. Weather perfect, everybody on lawn, Uncle George unmistakably Head of Family. Service with music beautiful and enjoyed by everybody of whatever denomination. Luiz more intent on watching bride and bridegroom than in performing ecclesiastical duties. Drove away after private farewell to Mother in bedroom; nobody supposed to come and see us off, but we weren't too surprised, on going up on deck to watch the ship moving away from the dock, to see quayside thronged with friends and relations, all waving madly. Stood on deck as ship sailed up the Thames, and saw the waving hands gradually disappearing. Realised that they had all gone and I was alone. Nobody was left—except Afonso. I was sailing away from home and from everything familiar; I was going to a strange home in a strange land. Afonso looked at me and said Only you and me, now. I said that suited me very well. My hand was on the rail, and he bent and put his lips on it, and kept them there for a little while, to the wonder and astonishment of onlookers. Later I said that I was going to our cabin to finish off Part 1 of my diary—which I'm now doing. The door will open soon, and for the first time, a man will have the right to come in and lie down beside me on the rather hard-looking bed with the blue-and-white striped cover. And if ever I had doubts before, I have no doubts now: with all my heart, I'm glad it's the first time—and with Afonso.

End of English girlhood and beginning of Portuguese wifehood, not to say motherhood. When the door opens, I'm ready and much, much more than willing.

Part 2

Tuesday June 20th.

Arrived at Lisbon on smart Italian ship, very different from tomato boat; the latter great mistake from honeymooners' point of view, as rolled non-stop all the way to Canaries; bride prostrated throughout what meant to be halcyon voyage. Bridegroom hale and hearty, bad beginning to marriage.

Beautiful calm morning. Wakened at dawn by Afonso, who took me up on deck to get first glimpse of Lisbon. Sea like glass, cool breeze, ship gliding silently, nobody on deck but ourselves. Lisbon in faint mist, looked lovely, set on hill and framed in green countryside. Ship drew nearer, could see cars passing on riverside road; nearer still, figures on dock now recognisable. Asked Afonso who likely to meet us, he said only Papa and Mama; Duarte in Brazil, José at sea, Vasco chasing girl in Venice, Alberto studying at Coimbra, Maria staying with fiancé's family in Oporto, Ana and Valeria gone with black-clad companion to family property in Algarve, Francisco and Luiz stayed at school in England. When ship almost alongside, saw Papa and Mama standing with (Afonso said) uncles and aunts. In due course all streamed up gangway: Mama, Papa, Uncles Antonio, Manuel and Pedro; Aunts Elena, Natalia and Guilhermina. Introductions, followed by formal procession to breakfast, self expecting snarl of protest from head steward, no snarl, on contrary, party received with courtesy and conducted to large reserved table on which Papa's name. Self ate toast, drank coffee; family got through eggs, fish and kidneys; made mental note to cut down Afonso's intake, though have to admit that so far haven't noticed any sign of obesity in family: aunts, like Mama, discreetly stout, but men thin not to say weedy. After meal, Afonso dispensed tips to appropriate ship's staff, and entire party proceeded down gangway to very noisy Customs shed. Aunts and uncles went away, Mama and I disassociated ourselves from sordid business of Customs examination. Mama asked if I had enjoyed Canaries; said yes, very much, didn't tell her that disproportionate amount of time on honeymoon spent by bridegroom in making bride practise Portuguese verbs. Luggage chalked, removed by porters; Afonso sent ahead in own car, pale blue two-seater with scarlet cushions and small fat chauffeur; self left to board enormous Daimler with Mama and Papa and tall thin chauffeur. Quay left behind, on to busy road flanked by yellow trams, on to Black Horse Square, Rossio and Avenida da Liberdade; not the shortest way home, but Papa anxious to show me something of Lisbon. Through wide, modern streets and narrow old twisting and very steep ones until finally came to district clearly recognisable as Best Residential. Car drove into large courtyard of imposing mansion and stopped before flight of marble steps; went up them and into vast hall; Afonso appeared, kissed me and took me to own rooms: large sitting room, bedroom with canopied double bed capable of accommodating Henry the Eighth and all wives; bathroom with pink marble floor and innumerable fitments. Maid appeared, proceeded to unpack our suitcases; was glad to see my hotch-potch of clothes removed for care and attention, both badly needed. Looked out of window, transfixed by view, stood entranced until enfolded in Afonso's arms and fervently embraced. Said I thought this lovely house, but when could we go to our own? He said after reasonable interval in which to meet relations who hadn't been able to come to our wedding. Lunch at 1.30: Mama, Papa, Afonso and self, Aunt Elena and Guilhermina, Cousin Ana, age about 23; her mother Aunt Isabel; Uncle Policarpo; this his surname but known as Uncle Poli because name Manuel and thus no confusion with Uncle Manuel. Uncle Poli small, thin, bald, bent and totally silent; thought he was deaf until noticed he heard every remark relating to food. Watched everybody, including Uncle Poli, put away lunch of heavy soup, fish in rich sauce, chicken-with-rice-and-peppers; reflected that if Afonso thought he was going to get meals like this in middle of day in our own house, Reinaldo, he had severe shock coming.

After lunch, entire disappearance of everybody; all reappeared for dinner, with addition of Ana, Valeria and black-clad companion known as Senhora Dona Beatriz; in all fourteen at table; Mama said with obvious sincerity that so nice to have little family party. Food good but heavy, cook in my opinion not up to Mother's and my standard. Papa said had no idea my Portuguese so advanced, all would now speak to me in Portuguese. Looked at Afonso for rescue, no rescue. After dinner, all assembled in drawing room, which large enough to allow complete separation between groups playing *fado* records or Bridge, sleeping or conversing. Senhora Dona Beatriz led me aside, welcomed me into the family, said had been with them since girl of eighteen, and how good, how sweet, how pious one and all. Cornered by Aunt Isabel, who imposing enough at distance but positively terrifying at close range: huge bare arms, huge bare-ish bosom, loud voice. Showed me photographs of her three grandsons aged three years, two years and three weeks respectively, children of Ana, now playing *fado* records; explained that she and Ana in England at time of my wedding, but unable to attend owing to imminent arrival of baby now aged three weeks; went on to say that Ana's husband in England on temporary business, but she had brought Ana and children back to Portugal as unable to endure casual not to say barbarous treatment meted out by English mothers to English babies, putting poor little things into prams exposed to elements and leaving to howl unattended until next meal. I explained English mothers of opinion that too much fondling spoilt babies; Aunt Isabel said that what spoilt babies was callous not to say barbarous treatment in infancy, as for instance leaving in prams to howl. I said English mothers busy, well-organised routine, many duties other than babies, such as washing-machine and preparation of meals. Aunt Isabel said babies of tender age not concerned with routine or fact that mother busy; little babies in need of love, love and more love, also warmth and security of maternal bosom; if I cared to ask any good doctor in Portugal, would learn that nothing adequate substitute for warm maternal contact, so Ana and little children now back in Portugal, where proper treatment of babies understood and practised. Was about to go in and bat for English mothers, when checked by disquieting memory of Uncle George's grandchildren howling in prams exposed to elements far from maternal bosom and next meal.

Bed at 10.45, thankful for stout door that closed behind Afonso and self, shutting out little family party. Asked Afonso if he agreed with his aunt Isabel's views on English babies, he said unable judge but curious fact no juvenile delinquency in Portugal; he had not hitherto connected this with warm maternal bosoms.

Wednesday June 21st.

Breakfast by ourselves on own little balcony in sunshine. Afonso out to lunch with Papa and man who has horse to sell; self with Mama to lunch with cracked aunt who under impression is Empress Joséphine. Driven to mansion only slightly less imposing than Mama's own; state progress into presence of very thin, very old lady with hair colour and consistency of beaten egg whites. Conversation, naturally, in French; no sign of craziness on part of hostess, but head of table at lunch laid for Napoleon, who unavoidably absent. On way home, Mama said would like to talk to me about my future home, Reinaldo; proceeded to say she and Papa hoped that Afonso and I would be very happy there, but certain things to explain:

1.Papa had bought property fifteen years ago from distant relation; about eight years ago had thought of reselling, as place took up more time than could afford to give, but Afonso opposed to sale, pointing out that he now knew as much if not more than Papa about property and could perfectly well manage it. Papa had agreed and Afonso had gone to live at Reinaldo.

2.Reinaldo estate well kept up, especially stables, which extensive, modern and excellent, but actual dwelling house not comfortably fitted or furnished, as before Afonso went to live there, never occupied for long periods; when family went there from Lisbon, chief pleasure of visit complete change from Lisbon conditions. When Afonso went to live there, Papa had offered to make alterations and improvements, but Afonso said that he liked the house just as it was. On his marriage, Papa had once again offered to alter or improve, but Afonso said no, changes, if any, better made by myself after seeing Reinaldo.

3.On death of Papa and Mama, Reinaldo property not only of Afonso but also of other nine children, unless Afonso by then sufficient money to buy out brothers and sisters, if brothers and sisters willing to sell their interest in property. Thus improvements, if carried out, not only for self and Afonso, but also for Duarte, José, Vasco, Alberto, Maria, Ana, Valeria, Francisco and Luiz.

4.Papa and Mama had therefore decided to let me see property before discussing changes; this little talk designed to make me understand that bare aspect of house not due to lack of interest on part of Papa and Mama, as both only too willing to help financially with whatever Afonso and I decided to do.

Thanked her, said, and meant, that very grateful for all her and Papa's kindness.

At 6.30, full-scale reception at house for all friends and relations unable to be present at our wedding. Champagne and two-tier wedding cake. Stood with Afonso in receiving line and then circulated with him among guests, two hundred, nationalities diverse. Afonso said only guests I need worry about were those living on neighbouring properties in Ribatejo. Met four neighbouring couples, Portuguese, all issued warm invitations to go and see them at any time and to let them know if could do anything at any time to help; lived very close, only four, five, nine and ten miles away respectively. Small, fat, shy, perspiring man brought to me by Mama and introduced as another neighbour, Senhor Freitas, only three miles away; he said please would I call him Manuel, as old friend of Afonso; his wife American, very eager to meet me, her name Jinny spelt with J, at present in America but returning soon, had sent her love to me. He himself not horses, but bulls; Jinny not interested in bulls, great pity. I wondered how unknown Jinny could have brought herself to marry small, fat, rather ugly Manuel; looked at him again and found to own surprise that beginning to like him very much. Interrupted by gaunt Englishwoman who said had received letter from my Uncle George, led me aside to say confidentially in loud voice that promised to keep an eye on me, as very difficult for young girl transplanted to foreign country, with foreign relations and foreign religion, especially as no intellectual life in Portugal; from point of view of questing minds, arid desert and food of course terrible. Rescued by fussy little Frenchman, who said he and wife, at present indisposed, had once met my mother's sister Blanche, now deceased, on cruise; small world, *n'est ce pas? Oui,* very. Rescued by two nice German girls who spoke German non-stop until Afonso, appearing, explained I didn't know any.

After reception, drove with Afonso along lovely moon-lit sea-edge to Cascais, where dined at restaurant overlooking Bay and gazed at lights twinkling on water. Afonso said was I happy? Said yes very, but at present had feeling of unreality, no job, nothing to do. He said plenty to do, young bride meeting friends and relations of husband, perfecting herself in his language, watching over his health and happiness; this far more real than my life in London, where merely sat in silly office typing letters of silly boss under illusion that this real independence; added that what myself and other girls observed by himself in London had called independence seemed to him nothing more than shedding of all responsibilities like mother, father, home and relations in order to earn pocket money in gay city without restricting supervision; added that I had now left this illusory existence and was about to shoulder responsibilities, not to mention for the moment privileges, of wifehood and motherhood. I said didn't want to spend rest of life merely giving orders, like his mother. He said that for intelligent girl, I sometimes displayed dismaying inability to see beyond nose; his mother very good, very sweet, very pious, also magnificent organiser managing house, estates, servants, children and dependent relatives with skill and tact and tirelessness; every moment of her day occupied. I said easy to sit down and give orders. Afonso said I must try sitting down and giving orders when we got to the Quinta do Reinaldo and see what happened, if anything. I said Reinaldo only few hours' drive, couldn't we go and look at it? He said no, out of the question, only week or two more in Lisbon and didn't want me to see it before going there as bride-to-future-home. Drove back to house; after Afonso asleep, lay awake trying to sort out impressions; saw foreign body, examined it, found it was homesickness. Felt tears trickling and thought how surprised Uncle George would be. Tried not to wake Afonso and then remembered he had married me for better or for worse, so woke him up and asked him to make me less homesick, which he did.

Thursday June 22nd.

Lunch at Estoril with Bridge-playing aunt; drove with Afonso along Marginal in brilliant sunshine, reached Estoril and passed Casino gardens and took wide road lined with magazine-cover houses. Aunt's house very pale pink, grey shutters, terraces and pergolas; garden riot of beauty and colour, but Aunt, when appeared, terrible shock as clad overall in black, with yellow hair, yellow face and yellow claws covered with rings. Conversation interspersed by aunt's anecdotes of local ex-Royalty, who, Afonso and myself led to believe, entirely dependent upon aunt for interesting company. Told Afonso on way home that he appeared to be running out of nice relations, so couldn't we leave for Reinaldo? He said would talk to Papa and fix a day.

Friday June 23rd.

Letter from Mother: lawn very dry, roses doing well except yellow ones near gate, Uncle George and Aunt Freda in Wales. Philippa at home, marriage postponed owing to Francis's father's refusal to take him into family firm. Dogs very well, hope Afonso and I too. Letter from Philippa: marriage postponed owing to beast of future father-in-law refusing place in firm, saying that Francis had told him to fill it and he had done so and had no intention of unfilling it again. Were there any jobs going in Lisbon? Letter from Afonso's sister Maria from Oporto: her fiancé's family very good very sweet very pious also very kind to her. Told Afonso I was very tired of this very good very sweet business; didn't his family ever say anything more astringent, not to say accurate? Afonso said that his parents had never allowed their children to speak unkindly of others. I said this very silly, as how could children learn to form sensible and fair judgments? My mother had not allowed unkind comment on physical defects or unavoidable handicaps, but had permitted discussion of likes and preferences in free and uninhibited way, which was the course I intended to follow with my own children, and would slap, hard, first one who said very good very sweet if object patently far from good and sweet. Afonso said no good crossing bridges until I got to them; I said this another thing my children wouldn't say, as heard it far too often from him, and all it meant was that he was too lazy or too Portuguese to do today what he could shelve until tomorrow. This speech far from effectual, being in Portuguese and subject to frequent corrections of verbs; decided that only way to be fluently abusive was to study the language at every opportunity; opportunity occurred during morning, as Afonso out with Papa; returned to say departure for Reinaldo fixed for one week from today. No time to rejoice, as late for lunch with Uncle Feliciano. Afonso said put on coolest dress, as very hot outside. Wore coolest dress, to find restaurant air-conditioned, first ten minutes arctic. Uncle Feliciano quite unlike rest of Mama's brothers; rather short, but imposing; likeness to somebody but couldn't be traced until realised exactly like photographs of Edward the Seventh in middle age. Drinks at the bar, after which Uncle Feliciano sent Afonso to check up on table; while Afonso doing so, Uncle Feliciano produced from pocket small jewel case and put into my hand, said this his wedding gift to me, couldn't send it to England so had kept it until now. Opened it to see brooch in form of fern, quite lovely. Thanked him all the more warmly as remembered harsh things had said about him to Afonso. Said would wear brooch now, Uncle Feliciano said no, diamonds looked better at night. Put case into bag, went into lunch; Uncle Feliciano chose food for all: avocado, crab salad and special veal dish made under his supervision at table. Bill paid by him by cheque. Told Afonso on way home that liked Uncle Feliciano very much, found him more man-of-the-world than other uncles, perhaps due to his being bachelor. Got home, showed brooch to Afonso and asked him to put it with other brooch in his steel box for safety; added was sorry to have thought that Uncle Feliciano was trying to get out of giving wedding present; hoped he could afford brooch but felt, personally, that so valuable a present should have been shared between Afonso and self, said that if Afonso liked, would accompany him to jeweller's and change it for something else, perhaps some silver dishes. No reply from Afonso; saw him leaning against chest of drawers apparently having fit. Went up to him in alarm, saw was convulsed with laughter. Asked what was funny, he said me. No further details available for some time, as unable to articulate; when able, took me in his arms and said couldn't imagine how had ever lived without me. I said would like to share funny joke. He said never dreamt he would marry girl who didn't know a diamond when she saw one, went on to explain that when I knew Uncle Feliciano better, would understand that this and similar presentations merely token; Uncle

Feliciano's instincts very generous, so would be very unhappy if unable to do everything he felt required of him, like giving lunches and diamond brooches. Lunch cheque today would be forwarded by restaurant to Afonso; brooch worth nothing in money, but worth a lot to Uncle Feliciano, who now happy at having played his part as rich and generous uncle. Afonso said was sorry I had thought brooch valuable, but knowing me, knew I wouldn't care anyway. Went on to explain further that Uncle Feliciano had long ago gambled away fortune and three of his four properties; fourth now kept up by small contributions from large numbers of the family, making large contribution in all; of this, reasonable income paid to Uncle Feliciano, rest kept by estate manager to administer estate; Uncle Feliciano kept out of debt by knowledge that if remaining property sold, would be man of no background, which not to be thought of. I said didn't mind in the least about brooch with fake diamonds and lunch bill sent to Afonso, and as far as I was concerned, Uncle Feliciano welcome to go on dressing up to look like Edward the Seventh and indulging generous instincts, but reserved to myself right to present him to my own children in his true light. Afonso said he and all his brothers and sisters quite aware of their relations' shortcomings, but no point in stripping veils from those who hid behind them; this not hollow pretence, as I seemed to think, but simply forbearance with weaknesses. Lay awake thinking about this, then woke Afonso and told him his Uncle Feliciano very good, very sweet, very pious dirty old crook.

Saturday June 24th.

Large lunch party given in our honour at restaurant, by Uncles Manuel, Antonio and Pedro; twenty-four at table, all close relations; not close enough to Mama to hear, but certain she was saying nice little family party.

Asked by Senhora Dona Beatriz if would very kindly speak English to Ana and Valeria as theirs far from perfect. Said I would; great relief to go from halting Portuguese to fluent English. Found not much to talk to Ana and Valeria about, as apart from French and German lessons from visiting professors, entire time devoted to latest *fado* records, latest hair fashions and latest dress fashions. Didn't notice any undue interest in opposite sex, asked Afonso why when Ana so lovely and Valeria so sexy, no long queue of suitors outside house ? He said suitors, yes, but this Portugal and not England, and certain formalities to be observed. I said was having Senhora Dona Beatriz tied to their tails one of the formalities, he said yes; young girls of good family in Portugal not free as girls of similar age and circumstance in England or America. I said or France or Belgium or Switzerland or Russia or the Netherlands, and wasn't it time the Anas and Valerias dropped the Senhora Dona Beatrizes into the local ponds? Afonso said this would come in time, no doubt, but at present Ana and Valeria not free to trip round Lisbon unaccompanied, or to entertain young men without Papa and Mama; added that in spite of this, I needn't feel that his two little sisters beating their wings, as both having lots of fun. I said what about jobs? He said lots of jobs, voluntary: teaching in schools run by charitable women, helping in hospitals, helping in orphanages. Added that should try to see life out here not through my own eyes but through my grandmother's; true that by some standards, this country convention-bound, but in my grandmother's day in England, not many girls went out alone, or took flats in town or left home to pursue career; moreover, when my grandmother settled down to run house and children, nobody accused her of being idle and useless. Added that progress would come and no doubt my children would have to look after their own children and do the shopping and wash the nappies and wheel the pram; having been reassured that my children not drones like his mother's children, perhaps I would do him a favour and sit back and try to cultivate art of leisure, lost elsewhere but still to be seen in Portugal.

Monday June 26th.

Woke with feeling of excitement, off to our own home tomorrow. Afonso went out to business lunch, self began packing. Afonso came back, said was getting a cold, sneezed once or twice during afternoon and sent to chemist for inhalant, throat pastilles and cough mixture, although no cough. Took his own temperature four times and said perhaps had better call doctor. As his temperature normal, I said why doctor? he said better have doctor at early stage. News of his indisposition spread through house, Ana, Valeria and Senhora Dona Beatriz came in to make kind enquiries, Mama came every half hour and laid gentle hand on sufferer's brow. I said so far nothing the matter with him except beginnings of cold; Mama said all his life subject to heavy colds, poor boy, accompanied by headaches, sore throat and feeling of lassitude. Felt like telling her that she needn't enumerate symptoms of common cold to anybody English. At 7.30, Afonso took temperature, found to mingled horror, pleasure and triumph that had risen half a degree. Mama entered with doctor, patient examined and pronounced to have cold. Heard, to my amazement, Mama asking how many days advisable to confine patient to bed; waited for laughing protest by Afonso; no laughing protest. Mama and doctor departed, Afonso lay back on pillows in dying-duck posture; told myself perhaps his symptoms beginning of something more serious than mere cold. Advised him to go without dinner, he said this very weakening. Door opened, Mama entered followed by large waggon followed by manservant; table put up beside bed, cloth, plates, cutlery, covered dishes containing shrimp soup, creamed fish, chilled asparagus, cold breast of chicken. Mama explained in aside that these Afonso's favourite foods, must tempt him to take a little something. Patient took everything. Mama, withdrawing, said would come back after dinner. On way downstairs with her, ventured to say thought this too much attention for common cold; she said Afonso subject to heavy colds, poor boy, accompanied by headaches, sore throat and feeling of lassitude; added that such a difficult patient, as impatient of fuss, anxious to get up and resume strenuous life. After dinner returned to own rooms, saw no sign on part of Afonso of ever wanting to get up again: low lights, clean sheets, clean pyjamas, thermometer in mouth; slept like log, ate breakfast of omelette and kidneys and pronounced cold alarmingly advanced. I took his temperature, found it dead on normal, told him could get up and resume strenuous life. He said all his life subject to colds. I said yes, accompanied by headaches, sore throat and feeling of lassitude, to say nothing of conviction that about to die. He said surprised to find me unfeeling. I said not unfeeling, but if he expected me to fly to his bed with chicken breasts every time he sneezed, quite mistaken. He said would I please send for doctor. I said would he like me to send for priest too, to administer Last Rites? He said perhaps I would like to occupy other rooms until he was better; in this way not inconvenienced by being expected to show sympathy. I said he was showing for first time Portuguese side of his nature. He said was Portuguese on both sides of his nature. Door opened, glimpse of Mama, door hastily shut. Afonso said there I went, shouting again, what would Mama think? Said I didn't care what anybody thought, all I wanted was to see him on his feet like a man, taking his wife to her future home and having cold like anybody else. Afonso said bitterly that he thought women ministering angels; I said would minister with zeal and affection when anything serious to minister to but could observe on this occasion only slight cold brought on by overeating. Afonso said would feel much better if I weren't in room; I said I would too. Went outside, saw Mama hovering, said was going in garden, would she please look after Afonso. Went into garden and sat in sunshine in front of little statue with fountain playing; began to cool down. Heard cries and saw Senhora Dona Beatriz gesticulating from upper window; took no notice. Little later, servant came out and proffered wide-brimmed straw hat; sent it back. Senhora Dona Beatriz came out, said dangerous to sit in sun in Portugal as sun's rays at such-and-such a slant, gave people sore throats. Said thank you, quite used to sun, never wore hat. Manner not encouraging; Senhora Dona Beatriz went inside, servant came out with larger hat; said go away and stay away. Felt conscience pricking, went upstairs and asked Afonso how he was; he said much worse.

Afonso slept well, I slept badly; didn't feel like breakfast, watched Afonso getting through his. Mama came to visit patient, asked me if I would go with Papa and herself to lunch with old family friend; found to my dismay my throat rather sore, but said yes thank you. Drove with them to house on other side of Tagus; enjoyed ferry crossing but realised throat getting worse, wondered if Senhora Dona Beatriz practised witchcraft. Lunch at lovely Quinta set in umbrella pines; found eating hard, talking harder. On way home, Mama said had I perhaps caught Afonso's cold? Said no, but by now feeling deathly. Got home, Mama took temperature, found it raging, said gently that dangerous to sit in sun in Portugal as sun's rays at such-and-such a slant, gave people sore throats. Got into bed, out of which Afonso leapt in alarm on my croaking and hot-cheeked return. Surrendered to all ministrations, asked Afonso to hold me in his arms as I passed away.

Saturday July 1st.

Didn't pass away. Lived to see Afonso devoting himself to me, entirely forgetful of self. Departure to Reinaldo now fixed for Tuesday 4th.

Maria came home from house of fiancé; fiancé came too, name of Jorge, rather small but good-looking, with large sad Portuguese eyes. Mama said Maria so lucky, Jorge and Jorge's whole family so good, so sweet, so pious. Asked if I would mind taking one or two little things to Reinaldo for her, as then less to take in September; had Afonso remembered to tell me that August impossible this year on account of Maria's wedding? Added that Papa lending station waggon for luggage, but some room in Uncle Poli's car for extra things. Uncle Poli's car? Yes, had Afonso forgotten to tell me that Uncle Poli going up to Reinaldo with us for week or two? Air so very good there, Uncle Poli needed change, and no trouble as took own servant. When in own room, asked Afonso why Uncle Poli couldn't have waited until we were settled at Reinaldo; he said must remember that Reinaldo not his house but Papa's, and therefore open to Mama's relations. I said would certainly remember this if he would remember that polite to mention to hostess that guests arriving before guests actually arrived.

Monday July 3rd.

Letter from Philippa: Francis thinking of going to Canada to start afresh, though not sure where, or what at; Philippa doesn't want to go; Francis offered job in Newcastle, doesn't want to go to Newcastle, Philippa said who would? Francis answered advertisement, job turned out to be in Wales, Philippa doesn't want to go to Wales, who would? Any jobs going in Lisbon? Afonso, after reading letter, said she and Francis probably the next uninvited guests at Reinaldo; felt apprehensive about this, wrote to Philippa telling her to go to Uncle George and ask his advice. Afonso, after reading letter, said that Uncle George's advice will be not to marry Francis.

Superintended packing; unpacked wedding presents again to show Maria, who away at Oporto at previous display. She said was longing to be married and devote life to Jorge and her children and be like Mama and Jorge's mother; Jorge's mother was going to be a nun before she met Jorge's father; this great bond between her and Maria, as Maria had thought of being nun before met Jorge. Asked Afonso later if this nun-or-wife attitude wasn't rather chilling for bridegroom? He said no, far from, as girl's religion very warm, passionate emotion, equally warm and passionate when transferred from Heaven to earth.

Day of departure. Got up and wrote rather incoherent letter to Mother, telling her new life now about to begin. Breakfast with family, Afonso irritatingly slow; decided he was being tactful and avoiding appearance of hurrying away. All at last ready; went outside and found courtyard like scene from War and Peace: family fleeing from approaching enemy. Afonso's car, and station waggon already loaded; saw that room for driver only in Afonso's car, learnt that self travelling in Uncle Poli's car. Entire family came out to say goodbye; Papa said station waggon overloaded. Thin and fat chauffeurs, assisted by Uncle Poli's chauffeur, unloaded it and redistributed load. Mama said picnic hampers placed by mistake in Afonso's car; Afonso's car unloaded, picnic hampers placed in separate cars. Afonso said where was new saddle? New saddle forgotten; fetched; Papa said had better go on luggage rack of Uncle Poli's car. Uncle Poli said No, *No,* NO, heavy weight on top of car would make steering difficult if not dangerous. At length persuaded that saddle quite light and would make no difference to steering. Saddle placed on luggage rack. Uncle Poli, assisted by attendant and chauffeur, placed carefully in car; procession at last on way: Afonso first, station waggon next, self and Uncle Poli last. Foot warmer placed at Uncle Poli's feet, car hermetically sealed, proceeded at 30 kilometres an hour in direction of Ribatejo. Uncle Poli fell asleep; self stared out of window and remembered dreams of driving swiftly to future home by husband's side. Tried to estimate how long would take, at this pace, to reach Reinaldo; reckoned eight hours. First part of journey along magnificent autostrada, but pace still funereal; road parallel to river Tagus, was surprised to find car actually passing boats going up-river. Crossed river at Vila Franca and drove along country road; car stopped, chauffeur got out, took off his cap, took out Uncle Poli, led him slowly to roadside bushes, hid him behind them, turned his back, surveyed scenery, counted twenty, retrieved Uncle Poli and packed him into car. Pattern repeated at half-hour intervals throughout journey. Looked out of window at passing scene and found myself revising ideas about Ribatejo. Had expected enormous grassy tracts; no grassy tracts of any size; road flanked by pinewoods, rice fields, eucalyptus groves, more rice fields, olive groves, vineyards and more rice fields. Arrived at Almeirim halted on outskirts at ornamental gate of beautiful Quinta to deliver flowers to lady owner who, Mama had hinted delicately, had in dim past rejected proposal of marriage from Uncle Poli. Thought that if lady saw Uncle Poli now, would have no reason to regret rejection. At 1.30, chauffeur drove car into pinewood, spread rugs, put up picnic table and chairs and served food; Uncle Poli ate chicken-with-rice-and-peppers, cold grilled sardines, cold omelette and cream cheese; watching him, decided that in spite of view generally held, over-eating couldn't or didn't hurry into early grave; Uncle Poli well over seventy but able to put away enormous meals with no sign of obesity, high blood pressure or fatty degeneration. Picnic over, Uncle Poli slept in car while chauffeur ate; I walked about in woods until all ready for continuance of journey. Country now more open; pastures interspersed between vines and olives; in distance horses and bulls. Looked at homesteads and wondered if ours like any of them. Passed Chamusca and proceeded in direction of Golegã, which Afonso had told me was *(a)* scene of annual horse fair and *(b)* point at which road to Reinaldo left main road. Reached Golega; not impressed. Felt heart sinking, only to bound upward as car stopped and saw Afonso beside us, now not in car but in Land Rover. Joyfully transhipped, sped ahead with Afonso, leaving Uncle Poli and hearse behind.

Left main road and immediately saw reason for Land Rover. Clung to Afonso, who said worse coming. He asked if country as I had imagined it; said no, had expected more of it; he said I had probably been thinking of Texas and not alluvial basin of Tagus. Drove for about an hour, then saw wide gate with wide gateposts; affixed to gate were letters which Afonso said were Papa's brand. Gates opened by *campino* in traditional dress, and cap with long tail; drove on, was filled with surprise to see not wide pastures but olives and vines and eucalyptus. Expressed this surprise to Afonso, who said extraordinary girl, first expected Texas and then imagined richest land in Portugal entirely given over to horses. I said ever since had known him, had heard him speak of Reinaldo but never, never had heard mention of anything but horses. Afonso said reason for this was that only horses interested him, but in taking over property, had naturally had to take over not only horses but vines and olives and sheep and mules, so now I could straighten out my ideas and view the reality, which was flat but also picturesque and productive; added that hoped I would like the feeling of space and the glimpses of the red roofs of neighbours far away in distance. Told him that liked everything already, but where were house and stables? He said house soon visible, but stables not, as two miles away behind slight rise in ground. Saw ahead, at end of dust track along which now driving, low white wall encircling group of low white houses. Roofs not red but terra-cotta; houses, in brilliant sunshine, almost blinding. Drove into enclosure and past casually-placed little white buildings. Brown earth, blue sky, no sign of gardens, but bougainvilia spilling over houses, plumbago climbing round windows and doors, islands of purple-red cannas and huge jars with pink and red geraniums. Everywhere, hens and turkeys and peacocks and fat black pigs and geese and women carrying pots on their heads; little brown children running beside Land Rover, waving and shouting to Afonso. Three or four more little houses, then a gap, then a bigger, longer white house.

Home.

Got out of car, met by group of people introduced by Afonso as aged cook, assistant cook, housemaid, parlourmaid, water carrier, wood hewer, poultry keeper and gardener. Had perhaps not been expecting trimly-uniformed staff of Lisbon house, but rather unprepared for homely bunch of peasants, women with scarves on heads surmounted by wide-brimmed straw hats, men in flat-crowned, wide-brimmed felt hats. Smiles apparent everywhere; speech of welcome croaked by ancient cook, said by Afonso to have been in charge of kitchen for past fifty-two years, aunt of assistant cook, who sister of housemaid, who married to gardener, who nephew to parlourmaid, who cousin of water carrier, who married to *campino*. Extricated by Afonso from web of relationships, led up three wooden steps into home.

Layout of house unorthodox, inconvenient but not complicated: wide, many-windowed verandah ran entire length of house; off this opened (left to right) bedroom, bathroom, bedroom, bathroom, bedroom, bathroom, bedroom, bathroom, combined drawing-dining room and then three more bedrooms and bathrooms. All bedrooms very small, all bathrooms very large. Every room without exception had door opening into adjacent room; thus possible to walk from one end of house to other without stepping on to verandah. All bedrooms, and living room, had windows looking on to back of house; all bathrooms had doors opening to back of house. Couldn't see any sign of a kitchen until led by Afonso back to living room, then saw that door led to kitchen built at right angles to rest of house. All floors stone. No curtains. Chair and sofa covers drab, furniture scanty and strictly functional. In bedrooms, iron bedstead, straw mattresses, two wooden chairs, marble-topped dressing chest; in living room, in addition to sagging sofa and chairs, big square dining table and innumerable wooden chairs ranged round walls like refugees' waiting room. All bathrooms with fittings Noah would have recognised. General effect: Stark Simplicity.

Led by Afonso to bedroom on extreme left, which ours; he asked if I liked our house. I said, with tear trickling down cheek, that loved it very much. And meant it. He said in worried tone, if pleased, why cry? Said because home with him at last, and come to a home which didn't have anybody else's stamp on it and which I could therefore make my own. He said perhaps he ought to have made it a bit more English for me, with cushions and curtains, but it had always been this way and as he spent so little time in it, had never bothered to change it, but I could go ahead and do what I liked. Short affectionate interlude interrupted by arrival of Uncle Poli, who conducted to bedroom at other end of house. Walked back to living room, inspected rag rugs on floor, noted every window fitted with fly-screens, every fly-screen rusty, out of shape and full of holes. Walked out to back of house, saw primitive tanks in which girl washing clothes; also poultry houses and large open shed in which cars kept, also Biblical bread oven. Wondered what gardener found to do, as no garden, no hedges, house giving impression of having sprung out of ground. Saw high bamboo fencing, opened gate and saw very large orchard-cum-vegetable garden; gardener, after all, plenty to do. Joined by Afonso; asked him which servants paid by us, which by Papa or estate; he said indoor servants paid by us, others paid from estate funds. Went into kitchen. Found it over-populated, both by humans and by flies. Aged cook came forward; asked her about dinner, was shown several pots hanging above massive open fireplace, and two or three more simmering on primitive clay stove. Pots contained brown soup, green soup, meat stew smelling strongly of garlic; watery concoction made from fish heads; green beans thinly sliced; pot roast and, in huge cauldron, about fifteen pounds of potatoes. Gathered that brown soup, fish lying on long wooden table, pot roast, beans and potatoes for High Table, rest for staff. Led to dubious-looking meat safe with broken screen door; inside, when flies brushed away, saw yellow mess said to be our pudding. Pointed to flies and to large holes in fly-screen of kitchen window and said must be mended; cook said would be done at once. Took large saucepan cover, brushed flies from fish on table, covered with saucepan lid; covered with cloth several large, flat, brownish loaves lying on side table; cook said she always kept everything covered, had uncovered for my inspection. Walked to table on other side, saw two large flat basins full of cold water, realised that no taps, here or elsewhere, water taken from row of Ali Baba jars standing beside table. Left kitchen, found Afonso in second bathroom from left, pouring cold water over himself and singing; he said first bathroom mine, this side of house entirely ours except when overflow of family or guests. Asked him about shopping, he said no shopping, fish sent up twice a week by Mama from Lisbon, sheep provided meat; fruit and vegetables, olive oil, wine and vinegar produced on estate, dry stores ordered by me by month from Lisbon. If anything required locally, housemaid's daughter, name of Inocencia, went on donkey to village two miles away and brought back whatever wanted, if available.

Message from Uncle Poli: he would dine in own room, kindly send in soup, chicken-with-rice-and-peppers, meat and cheese. Told Afonso dinner already prepared; Afonso said only seven o'clock, dinner not until eight, plenty of time to prepare chicken-with-rice-and-peppers, very good idea as he would like some too. Decided not to argue on first day, sent message to cook and shortly afterwards heard sounds of chicken-chase, asked Afonso why poultry houses so close to house, he said no idea, always had been. Rang handbell in bedroom, told housemaid Angelina to order bath. Twenty minutes later rang handbell again, asked Angelina where bath; informed on way. Ten minutes later, heard noise in bathroom, went in and got terrible fright, woman draped in black entering back door bearing on head can of apparently boiling water. Watched this tipped into clay bath and cold water added from Ali Baba jar; bathed, dressed and went to living room, where Afonso pouring drinks. Saw Uncle Poli's attendant carrying tray to Uncle Poli's room, ordered our own dinner. Pudding brought in looking diminished, as major portion eaten by Uncle Poli; Afonso displeased, as this, he said, his favourite pudding. I said that the flies had eaten as much of it as Uncle Poli, where could I get screening to renew completely useless screens all over house? Afonso said would have to send to Lisbon, but if I liked, could send to village to see if by chance any, but not to worry too much about flies, as so many here. I said wasn't worrying about them; was merely arranging to keep them out of house.

Wednesday July 5th.

Woke to find Afonso missing. Had bath, dressed, went to

kitchen to talk to cook about breakfast. Found entire staff seated at wooden table before bowls of coffee and hunks of bread; all rose at my entrance; I withdrew, cook followed me to see what I wanted, said to order breakfast. She said breakfast all ready, the Senhor always had the same breakfast, all now ready for him and for me. Told her I would have only toast and coffee, cook nodded, said would prepare at once. Eight-thirty, no sign of Afonso; nine, still no sign. At nine-thirty, sound of galloping hooves, went into verandah, saw beautiful sight: Afonso in tight trousers, short jacket and wide-brimmed hat, on magnificent horse, like trailer for cowboy film. Groom appeared, took horse; Afonso came on to verandah, couldn't kiss me as covered in dust, said would throw some water over himself and come to breakfast, dying of hunger. Sat down to breakfast at ten; huge pot of coffee placed before me with tiny jug of cold milk and four-inch-thick slice of bread scorched on both sides. Afonso got plate on which enormous omelette with tomato, potato, sliced green peppers and liberal sprinkling of chopped parsley. No butter on table, asked parlourmaid Mariana for some, after long interval Mariana appeared with saucer on which oily yellow mess. Afonso said pity no fridge, as no gas or electricity; was about to agree with him when noticed that his empty plate removed and dish made with chicken livers placed before him. Asked him, as he ate it, whether not somewhat unsuitable meal for warm not to say boiling hot morning of Portuguese July? He said had been in saddle for hours, had large hole inside, must fill; all very well for me to eat toast and butter. I said what toast and butter? He said must try and organise staff, especially kitchen staff; I said I certainly would, starting with the flies. Saw Mariana and Uncle Poli's attendant on way to his room with large trays, asked Afonso if all guests ordered own food and drink? he said in past, yes, because so much easier, and everybody satisfied; must remember that hitherto, he alone here and no time to bother about guests; added that I must go and change, as he wanted to take me down to the stables. Changed hurriedly, Afonso shouted for groom, groom appeared with Afonso's horse and rather pregnant looking one for me; Afonso said would choose me good horse and leave up here. Mounted not-good horse, Afonso said where was my hat? Said no hat suitable for wear with jodhpurs. He said hat essential, sent Mariana to his room; was made to wear wide-brimmed felt hat; too big for me, so crown stuffed with paper, after which not-good horse made strenuous efforts to keep up with superb animal bearing Afonso. Found myself suddenly with tremendous sense of well-being: handsome husband, even if given to over-eating; servants, even if untrained not to say raw; lovely home, even if at present drab and bleak; lots of space, even if rather flat and lonely-looking; gorgeous blue skies and lovely sunshine, even if perspiration making shirt stick to me; health and strength, even if at present undernourished owing to terrible toast and liquid butter. Began to sing; Afonso came closer, caught my rein and, still moving, kissed me; told me this first trick he ever learned on a horse.

Got to stables, pointed out to Afonso that horses far more comfortably housed than guests, not to say wife; rode with him from horse to horse, groom to groom, stable to stable. Sun got hotter and hotter, paper inside hat got wetter and wetter, hat got lower and lower; shirt now sticking altogether; as nothing underneath it, tried to hunch shoulders and draw in all-too-clearly-outlined bosom. Afonso said shouldn't have kept me out in heat so long, saddled a smallish, beautiful chestnut, handed not-good horse to groom, told groom to escort me back to house. Started back; chestnut and I had short sharp argument as to pace at which to return, chestnut won, I vanished over skyline, groom unable to escort as stuck with not-good horse. Chestnut proceeded at Derby speed to house, reared, shot me on to verandah steps and vanished in direction of stables. Staff, alarmed by sound of madly-galloping hooves, assembled on verandah in time to see ignominious descent; assisted to feet, ordered bath, shut self and wounded pride and lacerated person into bathroom. Came out, thought of ordering lunch, thought of not ordering lunch, sat down and wrote long letter to Mother. Asked her if she would, with money left by me in England, buy chintz, same pattern as bought recently for cottage, to cover sofa and two chairs, also for two smaller chairs. Told her house charming but needed more colour, was enjoying riding with Afonso. Went into kitchen to talk about meals, was shown pots simmering with fish stew, sheep stew, sheep-with-sausage and chicken-with-rice-and-peppers. Addressed cook and assistant cook Joséfina through buzz of flies, said flies must be got rid of; asked for fly-swats, no fly-swats. Made assault with rolled newspaper, no notable success. Said that man must be set to work mending fly-screens until new ones put in. Cook said man would come at once. Asked her about lunch and dinner, was led to cupboard or larder; saw on shelves tomatoes, onions, olives, figs, melons, mounds of quince jelly, rows of red and black sausages; on floor, sacks of potatoes, cabbages, carrots, turnips, green and red peppers. No flies, and lovely smell, mixture of garlic and peppers. Ranged against wall, jars of vinegar and olive oil. Had vision of self shopping in London during lunch hour: one lettuce, two toma- toes, two eggs and one tin baked beans; brought mind back to present plenty, said for lunch would have fried fish, cold meat and salad, cheese and fruit. Cook said what would the Senhor and the Senhor Dom Manuel like? I said fried fish, cold meat and salad, cheese and fruit; cook said yes, and what else? Said nothing else. Cook said please excuse, but the young Senhor all day on horse, very hungry; the old Senhor not strong, need- ed building up; myself far, far too thin, needed good nourish- ment, why no appetite? Had made for the young and the old Senhor mutton stew, fish-with-potato and caramel custard but if I didn't like any of this, why not let her make me nice nour- ishing dish of chicken breasts stewed in butter and served with semolina cooked in chicken stock ? if so thin, how have large family of babies and nourish them? had been over fifty years in this kitchen, knew tastes, needs, preferences and dislikes of every member of family, had always managed very well without orders, which only unnecessary trouble for me; as I could see, everything in kitchen in perfect order, nobody but herself allowed to touch food supplies, which carefully guarded, sparingly used and faithfully accounted for; I could rest assured that no need to think about kitchen, as all running smoothly; I could place utmost confidence in cook and be free to pass time enjoyably without worrying over household matters; Angelina and Mariana did everything she told them, so I could leave matters in her hands as the Senhora Mother-of-Senhor had always done. Couldn't think of anything to say to this, so withdrew. Asked Afonso at lunch (mutton stew, fish-with-potato and caramel custard) how Uncle Poli could benefit by change if shut in room all day? Afonso said seldom came out of it, but enjoyed being with us, even if didn't see us.

After lunch, had heavy luggage brought on to verandah; began to unpack. Started on books, discovered that no shelves to put them on. At dinner (vegetable soup, fish-with-rice, mutton stew and naked bananas swimming in yellow syrup) said nowhere to put books, china, glass or ornaments; Afonso said must send for carpenter and tell him what I want.

Thursday July 6th.

Went in Land Rover to village. Shopping list:

1 dozen fly-swats.

Fly-screening.

Salt and pepper containers to replace hideous ones in

form of pigs now on table, none given as wedding presents.

Large jug for hot milk.

Towelling to make into kitchen towels.

Got to village. No swats, no screening, salt and pepper in form of pigs only, no suitable jug. Bought towelling and went home. Roads very dusty, surfaces unspeakable. Got home, Mariana said her mother would come and make towelling into towels. Asked if carpenter had come; no carpenter. Said that message was to be sent again, this time stronger. Sat on verandah with my cookery books, making menus. At lunch, told Afonso worried because no letter from Mother for ages, in fact no post at all. Afonso said had I sent for it? I said sent for what? He said the post. I said did he mean to say he had been sitting here all this time expecting me to divine that mail had to be sent for? He said did I think a postman would trudge to the remoter Ribatejo estates? I said yes, I did think. Afonso said very silly, of course post had to be sent for; Mariana's brother used to fetch, but got married and now lives in Tomar so can't fetch any more; he would see if Joséfina's son could go. Joséfina sent for, asked to produce son; afternoon went by, no son. Joséfina said yes, son coming at once. At dinner, Afonso said had met Joséfina's son on way to house, but too late to get mail, was going to fetch it tomorrow.

Friday July 7th.

Three letters from Mother, one from Uncle George, two from Philippa. Settled down on chair on verandah to read, read that Mother had had no letter from me for long time. Stopped reading, found Afonso in bath, said where were the letters I'd written to Mother since coming to Reinaldo and given him to post? Afonso said terribly sorry, entirely forgot, had put them in usual place but quite forgot that Mariana's brother now married and living in Tomar. I said that now we had established where Mariana's brother is, would he kindly tell me where my mother's letters were? Afonso said had put them in the usual place behind picture in hall, where all mail put and duly taken out every day for posting, except this time not taken out because of Mariana's brother having got married and gone to live at Tomar. Went to picture, took down letters, tried to control rage, couldn't, went back to bathroom and told Afonso what I thought, which language he said only suitable for bathroom. Asked him if from this god-forsaken spot could send telegram of reassurance to my Mother; he said why reassurance? no news good news, but if Mother anxious, which he didn't think likely, telegram could be sent by telephone. Sent telegram, went back to ask Afonso if had ordered fly-screening from Lisbon, as asked him to yesterday. Pause; he said very sorry, very busy, no time to think of little thing like fly-screening.

Unexpected pleasure, if pleasure, of Uncle Poli's presence at dinner; came in unannounced, ate without uttering, got up, bowed, took attendant's arm and shuffled out. I said who was that man? Afonso said appearance at dinner sign of great affection. Asked whether any chance of his ever leaving us; Afonso said not yet, but nobody could say poor old man any trouble.

Saturday July 8th.

Reminded Afonso about fly-screens. Went on short walk round house, met and made friends with men, women, babies and dogs, saw in disused shed several nice-looking cane chairs; gave orders for these to be taken up to our verandah, as thought would look very nice painted pale yellow and covered with gay cushions. Found carpenter waiting for me with his tools already spread over verandah; gave him sketches and measurements of shelves and transferred his workshop to bedroom next to Uncle Poli's. This bad move, as Uncle Poli, coming out of his room to complain, saw chairs on verandah and installed himself on most comfortable one, with pillows below, rugs above and small tables with water, milk and medicines all round. His lunch served on verandah, Afonso said this never known before, great sign of affection. Asked if fly-screening ordered, Afonso said sorry forgot, but if I ring up, Aunt Isabel will bring up, had he forgotten to mention that letter from Aunt Isabel saying would like to come up for week or two with middle grandchild who had bad cough? Said forcibly that didn't want and wouldn't have Aunt Isabel and coughing grandchild, had enough on my hands with unorganised kitchen owing to not liking to cut down Uncle Poli's food, no unpacking as nowhere to put anything, no shelves for books or ornaments or china or glass, no decent cupboards for clothes, no towel rails in bathrooms for wedding-present towels, no linen cupboard for sheets and pillow cases, everything still in packing cases and likely to remain there for rest of married life and therefore not prepared and in no mood to receive hordes of relations. Afonso said hush or Uncle Poli might hear and think we didn't want him, at present guests perhaps unwelcome but this place very lonely and time would come when I would welcome company. Said the time hadn't come yet; Afonso said in that case, wished he hadn't told Aunt Isabel she could come and bring grandchild.

Sunday July 9th.

Slight fall of rain after long period of unbroken sunshine; bad night owing to mosquitoes; self not bitten, but Afonso unable to sleep, said eaten alive, woke me up to tell me that least I could have done was have screens mended, plenty of fly-screening down at stables, all I had to do was ask instead of letting matters slide until one mass of bites.

Monday July 10th.

Three men rode up from stables carrying rolls of fly-screening. Carpenter sent for assistant, set to work mending or replacing all screens round house. Fly-swats made by cutting small squares of fly-screening and affixing to lengths of wood; self, assisted by Joséfina and Mariana, went on fly-slaughtering campaign, beginning in kitchen. Told cook while there that in future she must come to me every morning for day's orders; today's lunch would be mutton chops, green beans, puree of potato, and salad of tomato and watercress. Cook said yes, what else? Said nothing else, very hot day, light meal desirable. Cook said please excuse; the old Senhor, I was given to understand, not interested in temperature, only in food; I said in that case she could make some fish cream and serve it to the old Senhor before his mutton chop; for dinner, tomato soup, baked fish, roast leg of mutton, chocolate mousse.

Kitchen towels finished; had intended to use own machine but found, on unpacking, that owing to lamentable mistake on part of shop, had been supplied with electric one; towels therefore machined on ancient hand-machine belonging to Mariana's mother.

Two shelves made, living room beginning to look lived in. Lunch not success, chops tough, potato lumpy. Afonso not impressed; message from Uncle Poli to say interference entirely uncalled for. Dinner disastrous: soup all right, fish all right but English way of roasting not understood by cook, meat reduced to dry fragments, chocolate mousse unrecognisable. Afonso said no use trying to run before cook could walk. I said all I wanted from him was patience. He said would be patient, but not if half-starved, please to remember not sitting at office desk but leading strenuous life.

Tuesday July 11th.

English breakfast of eggs, toast and coffee. Afonso said

did I expect him to cope with heavy day's work on that? Ordered omelette for him. After breakfast, Uncle Poli's packing done, car ordered; after brief farewell, departure with attendant. Telegram from Aunt Isabel in evening: grandchild's cough better, had decided after all not to come.

Wednesday July 12th.

More shelves up, food still terrible.

Thursday July 13th.

Man painting verandah chairs. Drove to village, bought straw stuffing for cushions and material to cover; sent for Mariana's mother to come and make. Afonso busy, out almost all day except for meals, which though now larger, not well cooked.

Saturday July 15th.

Dinner with neighbours eight miles away; Portuguese. House two-storied, ugly but comfortable, reached by tarred road and lit by electricity. Dinner good but heavy; hostess's four little children present at meal; watched them eating heartily and thought of Uncle George's grandchildren sitting down to cornflakes, milk and biscuits. Conversation: bulls and babies.

Monday July 17th.

Afonso still very busy, now home for hasty lunch, and dinner silent meal owing to fact of his being half asleep; after dinner, bed and Afonso instantly fully and deeply asleep. Said as able to spend so little time with me, why didn't I leave house more and join him outside?

Tuesday July 18th.

Rode out in search of Afonso; didn't find. When eventually found, was sent home by him, as he said now far too hot for me to go out of doors after mid-morning. Cupboard made for glass and china; put glass and china in, put ornaments on top, lit lamps, effect lovely, longed for Afonso to come in and see; Afonso came in, didn't see. Dinner at neighbours, conversation babies and crops, house only just above flood level but well heated and comfortable, lit by electricity, American-type kitchen.

Thursday July 20th.

Taken by Afonso down to circular track where horses being trained to jump; placed at fence and told to yell when horse approached, to encourage over fence. Horse approached, yelled. Horse stopped. Yelled some more, horse shied. Told him not to be a fool, to get over that fence. Horse laughed. Afonso came up, said this no good, he only brought me because thought I might be useful, must do better. Another horse galloped round, sailed over all fences, came to mine, stopped dead. Sent home by Afonso.

Friday July 21st.

Dinner five miles away at rice-growing neighbours, Portuguese, several children but all away at school. Long tarred road to house, entrance brilliantly lit (electricity) drive full of cars, drawing room ornate but effective, guests all neighbouring families assembled to meet us. Wide archway led to dining room with dining table under flashing not to say flashy chandeliers. Began to realise that Reinaldo the Cinderella of district but didn't say this to Afonso on way home, for fear of hurting his feelings.

Saturday July 22nd.

Morning visit from neighbour; led her to drawing-dining room, ordered coffee and biscuits, remembered no biscuits. Carpenter hammering, machine whirring, visitor (owner of chandeliers) said how nice to have house like this, so simple, so typical, asked me to go over and see her whenever could, so nice to have someone young, most wives, like herself, not so young.

Monday July 24th.

Showed cook for fourth time how to do roast mutton; prepared it with her and told her not to overcook. Finished product dry as bleached bones, Afonso said why not stick to Portuguese way of cooking? I said why not face fact that for last fifty-two years cook queen of kitchen, couldn't cook in first place and now no intention of learning, why not pension off? Afonso said better to wait until Mama came up. I said why? He said his mother better able to deal with cook, having known her so long. I said cook either mine or his mother's, which? Afonso said of course mine but better not to do anything in hurry. I said not prepared to wait another fifty-two years, and no question of throwing cook out to starve, as had several thriving relations on estate, as well as two-roomed house of her own for life; added that no use trying to teach new dishes, owing to impossibility of supervising beyond preparation stage; once dish in primitive clay oven or suspended in cauldron over fire, am unable to cope. Asked Afonso why, when electric grids visible all over Tagus basin, no electricity ever brought to this house? He said nothing softer, nothing more restful than lamplight, loved coming home to glow of lamps in winter. I said electricity could be confined to kitchen, but words lost in cloud of dust as Afonso vanished in direction of stables. Clouds of dust now part of life, as strong breeze blowing non-stop and sending quantities of Ribatejo topsoil on to new shelves, new cupboards, books and glass and china.

Saturday July 29th.

Dinner party for neighbours, sixteen at dinner; planned clear soup, fish cream, duck, and lemon meringue. Soup not clear, fish lumpy, duck though dead capable of breaking guests' teeth, lemon meringue floating mass of egg white on mustard-coloured sea. Remembered delicious meals served in cottage, cooked by self and Mother. Also remembered delicious meals served in flat in London, cooked by me alone. Coffee on verandah, newly-covered chairs admired, guests, between bull, horse and crop conversation, said what charming house, so simple, so typical. When guests gone, Afonso said dinner not up to much, didn't I think it time to give up trying to cook silk purses with sows' ears? Said yes, I did think so. Afonso said neighbours all very nice, why didn't I go and see them and learn from them? I pointed out that myself not in need of instruction, only cook. Went to bed, lay awake staring into terrible future, sea of dust, uneatable food, no young society, complete forgetfulness of native tongue, passionate love-making mere brief sessions on squeaky straw mattress, and husband turning into horse before my very eyes. Yearned for home, realised no longer home without Afonso. Longed desperately for uninhibited chat with Philippa. Longed for old friends, even Clara Cornhill. Afonso woke up, took me in arms, asked if happy. Said for moment, no, but adjustment slow process. He said loved me very much, couldn't live without me. I said that unfortunately for me, couldn't live without him.

Tuesday August 1st.

Stuffed more cushions for verandah chairs. Told cook must try to do better, cook said had never been asked to cook foreign food before, willing to do best in Portuguese. Afonso not in to lunch, mare foaling; late for dinner, dinner terrible. Prayed for someone I could talk to, someone of my own sex, own age, own tongue.

Wednesday August 2nd.

Prayer answered. At 10.30, expensive-looking car drove up; chauffeur cap in hand, opened door. Girl got out: slim, small, oval face, not pretty but piquante, large brown eyes, soft red discontented mouth, white dress, white band round hair, wide white belt, large white bag, bare brown legs, flat-heeled silver sandals. Before could take in dazzling whole, heard casual American voice telling me that this Jinny Freitas, I didn't know her, but did I remember her husband? short and fat and very ugly, but ugly or not, she loved him.

Asked her to come in. Was about to try to explain what her arrival and the sight and sound of her meant to me, when she said that the sight and sound of me almost more than she could bear, unutterably relieved to have someone young to talk to at last, especially in English, as although married for four years, incredibly, to Manuel, knowledge of Portuguese practically limited to telling people she didn't know any. Had longed for someone like me; neighbours all no doubt well-meaning, but middle-aged and pregnant, and as she herself barren, nothing to talk to them about. No, thank you, no coffee, no nothing, just listening to me was Heaven, was I going to do anything about this frightful house? She had seen it when brought here to dine when first married, had thought it a nightmare and said so and didn't really feel Afonso had liked her since, but truth was truth and everybody thought Afonso very mean to bring unsuspecting English bride to cabin-in-woods type of home when perfectly well able to afford improvements; which reminded her, she'd once met someone I knew, name of Philippa Something, wasn't she going to marry Francis Welby, if so, someone ought to warn her off, as he only one degree removed from certifiable; she must go now, heavenly to stay here and talk to me, but if away from Manuel for long, he liable to fit of melancholia, so different from most of local husbands, always of course excepting Afonso; did I know that he never looked at anybody before he married? all the same, I ought to keep an eye on him, not over women but over horses; if his children were born with two legs, he'd think they were freaks. Horses, bulls and rice; such Heaven to have me here, was I free tomorrow ? if so, why not go into Lisbon with her, she was going to the hairdresser. I said sorry, no. She said why not come after lunch day after tomorrow, she would send her car for me and then Afonso could come and dine and take me home. Said thank you, would like to go. Jinny got into car, was driven away; Afonso said at lunch had seen Manuel Freitas' car; I said Jinny Freitas had called. Afonso said pity that Manuel, who really nice fellow, had married girl with no brain, had she bored me ? Said no, she hadn't bored me and had invited us to dinner day after tomorrow. Afonso said would go this time but would like to avoid Jinny on the whole, as didn't care for her,

her tongue far too long.

Thursday August 3rd.

Letter from Mama, wedding preparations well in hand, longing to see self and Afonso, must fix early date for our arrival in Lisbon, as anxious for us to meet all Jorge's relations.

Letter from Mother: curtain and chair material sent off.

Postcard from Philippa: no job yet but decided to get married anyway, wedding with close relations only, hoped Francis's father would relent at ceremony and offer job.

Letter from Vasco: had met very nice Swedish girl, could we ask her to Reinaldo as she hoped to tour Portugal. Afonso said write at once and say no, Vasco's nice girls mixed lot, came to stay with alacrity and departed with reluctance.

Afonso said verandah chairs nice but cushions very hard, why straw for stuffing? I had only to ask cook, who had unlimited down from generations of dead ducks.

Friday August 4th.

Jinny's car arrived after lunch, driven by Jinny; proceeded at high speed along bad roads, Jinny said didn't see why shouldn't have full use of car while it lasted. Sped through little white villages; inhabitants, warned by musical signal on horn, scattering to right and left. Just beyond fourth white village, saw high, beautiful iron gate through which glimpse of long and lovely drive between tall eucalyptus. At end of drive, graceful white house, long flight of steps, open entrance hall with pink marble floor, arches on every side, whole effect rich and rare. Sat and talked in large drawing room with antiques on every side, until taken by Jinny to her bedroom, where watched her change into dress for afternoon, assisted by neatly-uniformed maid. She asked how many neighbours I had met; gave her details; she said she not popular in district owing to impossibility of being able to confine her conversation to matters domestic; local families large, women either had or about to have children and cared to talk only about them or about servants. Asked if Afonso's family coming up in August, I said no, owing to wedding of Maria. Jinny said supposed was marrying that little Jorge? Said yes. Jinny said nice little man but not strong enough to prevent himself from being swallowed up by Maria's family; Maria very pretty but short on personality, in fact didn't I find the whole family rather tepid, always excepting Afonso? Said found them very kind; Jinny said nice of me to stick up for them but disgraceful, with all their packets of money, to let me live at Reinaldo like peasant; had talked for years about putting in improvements, but had I discovered yet that the Portuguese never do anything they can get out of doing? When the Spanish said *mañana* they very often meant *mañana* but when the Portuguese said *amanhã,* all they meant was that if the thing was ignored, it would go away; in other words, if left until tomorrow, somebody else would do it or, better still, it wouldn't need to be done at all. This latter, Jinny added, maddeningly often the case, but she had

115

made a point all her married life, even when on morrow had changed her mind, of sticking to original intention in order to keep Manuel up to scratch. Couldn't of course advise me, but would like to warn me that if left to Afonso, Reinaldo would remain in primitive state for rest of time, up to me to blast him into doing something about it; such a pity I hadn't come out before I was married, to take a look at the place; that's what she had done, taken a quick trip with an aunt, to see what she was letting herself in for. Just as well she did, as house furnished entirely by Manuel's mother, if I had ever seen her, no further words would be necessary. Jinny said had told Manuel what to throw out, which was practically everything, and had brought over with her everything I now saw round me except fittings, which made to her order in Lisbon. Asked whether Ana and Valeria engaged; said no. Jinny said pretty girls, but nothing in heads. I said liked them very much. Jinny said nice of me to keep sticking up for family, but she had found easier in long run to speak plain truth; Manuel much happier, much freer since she proved to him that his mother nothing but old cow; Manuel now much better son, as very capable of tending and managing old cows. Rest of time before dinner spent in trying on Jinny's dresses and looking over garden. Afonso came at about 7; drinks and dinner in picturesque courtyard with fountain playing. On way home, Afonso said relief to get away, Manuel nice fellow but wife catty little clothes horse. I said must give her credit for lovely house; Afonso said why? perfectly all right before she came along and filled it with untypical furniture, and who wanted to eat dinner listening to a fountain going glub glub glub? I said was getting tired of this word *typical,* what did it mean anyhow? Afonso said it meant a house in keeping with its surroundings, as with early American settlers. Added that he had known that as soon as Jinny Freitas got hold of me, I would start a campaign for luxurious living, and here it was, starting. I said all I wanted was a decent stove in kitchen, and a fridge; the rest could for the moment remain as typical as before. Added that stove could be gas, with gas cylinders such as had seen in shops when driving to Reinaldo; gas fridges also available. Afonso said did I know what a gas stove and a gas fridge would cost? who was going to pay for them ? I said he had sold two horses last week, what about using that money? He said, in shocked tone, money not his to use; belonged to estate and went back into estate. I said house important part of estate, also that Papa and Mama had promised to help with improvements. Afonso said why not let cook go on cooking on stove she was used to, and understood? I said I had no hope of raising standard of food unless could demonstrate, and utterly unable to demonstrate in present kitchen. Afonso said when first showed me Reinaldo, I had said liked it very much. Said yes, but had given no guarantee that would leave it untouched for ever, and could I have horse money for gas stove and gas fridge? Afonso said no, that money Papa's. Nothing more said on subject until in bed, when Afonso, blowing out lamp, said in bitter tone hadn't realised I was easily-influenced type, would have thought I could have seen through hollow piece like Jinny Freitas, who idle, selfish and a malicious gossip. I said on contrary, Jinny very good very sweet very pious.

Tuesday August 8th.

Carpenter finished shelves in drawing room, painted white, filled with books, place beginning to look very nice but bare without curtains. Told Afonso at lunch that pity material not yet arrived; he said what material? I said material for curtains being sent out by Mother. He said WHAT in loud voice, choked over food, stared and asked when sent. I said had written to ask shortly after arriving at Reinaldo. Afonso in despairing voice said why hadn't I spoken to him first, and had I told Mother that vitally important to write *Old Clothing Only* on all packages? Said no, hadn't asked for old clothing, only for curtain material. Afonso said why couldn't I have bought curtain material in Lisbon like everybody else? Said because had found Portuguese chintz unsuitable and imported chintz too expensive; he said wait and see what my imported chintz cost when duty paid if not marked *Old Clothing Only*—but better not to worry now; would I please consult him before taking these steps? Said I would, but never imagined would have to ask him before asking my own mother to send me something paid for with own money.

Wednesday August 9th.

Went with Afonso in Land Rover to Santarem, to see possible mule buyer and put horse money in Bank. While business in hand, wandered alone round pleasant flower-decked squares and enjoyed extensive view of surrounding country, then walked back towards restaurant where meeting Afonso for lunch. After lunch, sat in Land Rover while Afonso bought bits and bridles. After short time, noticed that Land Rover parked outside shop, window of which entirely full of gas stoves. Stared longingly, thought how wonderful to go in and buy one, only no money, own small capital left at Afonso's request to be invested in England, and half-year's interest eaten up by curtains and chair covers. Put stoves out of mind, tried to think of other matters, couldn't, only thought in head sudden realisation of fact that Afonso and I had Joint Account in Bank at Santarem; thus, if he could put in, couldn't I take out?

Got out of Land Rover, went into shop. No bother buying stove, slight check about gas cylinders as necessary to sign papers. Signed them, wrote cheque, remembered suddenly that horse money probably not paid into Afonso's account but estate account, too late to worry, not worried anyway, signed cheque and had gas stove and gas cylinders loaded on to Land Rover, went back to shop to find out name of future supplier of cylinders. Got into Land Rover, saw Afonso coming, lost nerve and said earnest prayer for preservation of happy married relations. Saw with surprise Afonso walked past Land Rover, realised hadn't recognised it with unfamiliar load. Saw him stop and turn. Renewed prayers with increased fervour. Opened eyes to see Afonso standing beside Land Rover trying to speak. No words. Saw him get into Land Rover and sit at wheel staring straight ahead, still no words. I said in desperate voice, did he love me? He turned to stare at me and after long consideration, said yes. I said had just prayed to Our Lady—*his* Lady—for indulgence on part of husband, so was Afonso going to do Her out of opportunity of granting prayer? Afonso, after long pause, said what right had heretic to ask for favours? I said had addressed prayer to Our Lady—*his* Lady—of Fatima, as while in Portugal, considered Her responsible for well-being of all Portuguese wives, heretics or not. Afonso, after thought, said very difficult position for him, as if prayer not granted, door to closer approach to Her might be barred. I said this very good point. Afonso, kissing me before interested passers-by, said loved me so much that it hurt. I said that what hurt was thought of telling Papa, this I would do. Afonso, kissing me again, said no, he would, and may Our Lady, his Lady, help us both.

Drove home. Gas stove and cylinders carried into kitchen, cook not present. Message brought later, cook very ill, had decided too old for work, was now in house of nephew but would call in morning to bid formal farewell and remove own belongings.

Went into kitchen, promoted assistant cook Joséfina, and set to work. Dinner: cold vichysoisse soup, chicken in casserole with snowed potatoes and creamed spinach, beautiful lemon meringue pie with crisp pastry, succulent filling and meringue of pale gold. And in case Afonso still unfilled, delicious Swiss *fondue* on small squares of toast. Afonso, deeply moved, opened bottle of champagne hidden from me in bottom drawer of dressing chest. Later, blowing out lamp, he said was sorry had not bought gas stove himself. Forgave him. Woke him up later to say forgot to tell him had prayed to Our Lady, *his* Lady, for gas fridge.

Thursday August 10th.

Urgent appeal from Mama by post, begging me to come down early, great deal to be done still in way of wedding preparations, would be so nice to have me. Afonso, reading letter, said this nonsense, as Mama plus numerous assistants perfectly well able to cope, this simply excuse to get us both down, as obvious I wouldn't go without him. I said not so obvious, Lisbon nice change for horses. After discussion, decided to go down on 22nd, quite soon enough for wedding on Sept. 2nd. Told Mama this by phone, suggested her and Papa coming down tomorrow for long weekend, to get nice rest before embarking on final wedding preparations. She said love to come but couldn't spare time; Papa came to phone, said very kind suggestion, would bring her down for nice long weekend of rest and relaxation.

Jinny came to say goodbye, as going to England to join in family celebrations resultant upon long-awaited elevation of uncle to peerage. At end of visit, walked with her to car and said wasn't her uncle Chairman of that car group and if so, couldn't she get him by himself and ask him to give Francis

Welby a job? She said was I crazy? Francis Welby practically certifiable; I said yes, but was going to marry Philippa and needed job badly as how support wife when nothing to live on? Jinny said would do her best, but if her uncle mentioned qualifications, what would she say? I said that newly-elevated Peer brimful of champagne would probably bypass essentials, was just a matter of choosing right moment. Jinny said mean trick to play on poor old man; when he came to and found Francis Welby in his firm, he'd probably throw fit and chew up his strawberry leaves.

Friday August 11th.

Letter from Mother; had received wedding invitation from Mama, so kind but quite impossible accept, trip very expensive and money better saved for future visit. Felt depressed, but Afonso pointed out that Mother saving up to come and see our children, if came out for wedding wouldn't enjoy ceremony owing to having paid so much to get to it. Papa and Mama for weekend; arranged with Afonso that nothing to be said about gas stove until after dinner; if dinner as good as hoped, would take Mama on to verandah, leaving Afonso to break news of how dinner cooked and how stove paid for. Dinner superlative. Took Mama on to verandah, couldn't bear to leave confession to Afonso, so told Mama; at same moment, Papa came out, much amused, and said must all go into kitchen and inspect new stove. Self complimented on improvement, Joséfina complimented on cooking.

Saturday August 12th.

Spent morning helping Mama sort wedding-invitation list and replies. She said so nice to have me in family, so efficient, so unselfish, so helpful, how my own mother must miss me, hoped I was learning to love Reinaldo, as whole family had always loved it, so quiet, so remote, so simple, so typical; Afonso had in fact wanted to bring me on honeymoon here, but dissuaded by Papa, as though perfect place for honeymoon, in my case was going to be future home, such a pity we couldn't have offered it to Maria and Jorge, Maria not likely to enjoy honeymoon anywhere else, as always dreamt of honeymoon at Reinaldo. I said pity about that, if had known in time might have arranged something. Mama said how kind, how unselfish, must go at once to Papa and tell him of kind and unselfish suggestion. Went. I went in search of Afonso, told him simple remark mistaken for invitation to Maria and Jorge to spend honeymoon here. Afonso said in angry voice that quite out of question, one thing for house to be available for honeymoon couples in days before he married, but now his home, also mine, with all our things round us and shelves made and furnished and everything at last running smoothly and kitchen under control, never in his life heard such ridiculous suggestion as turning out for Maria and Jorge, especially as Jorge rich enough to buy up neighbouring properties for honeymoon, impossible for Mama to have taken me seriously. Said not impossible, but was glad to know that he thought of Reinaldo as our home and not merely as extension of Lisbon home. He said I knew perfectly well had always longed to settle, repeat settle with me at Reinaldo; one thing to take time off for attending wedding of sister, but quite another thing to abandon home for long additional period in order to please Jorge, whose only knowledge of horses which side to mount. Interrupted by Papa, who came to say how kind, how unselfish. Interrupted by Afonso, who said in firm voice misunderstanding; in his opinion, utterly impracticable idea, as Reinaldo now our home, and people couldn't expect us to turn out of home in order to hand over to honeymoon couples, however closely related. Papa said this quite true and Afonso quite right to point it out; only one special circumstance in present case: Maria's last chance to enjoy Reinaldo. Afonso said not her last chance at all, she and Jorge could drop in at any time, but not for honeymoon; impossible for us to be asked to give up our home every time one of his brothers or sisters got married. Before his marriage, different, but now had me to think of. Papa said that in that case, nothing more to be said, very pleased to find Afonso so home-loving; now no question of turning us out, simply kindly impulse on my part for which deserved great gratitude, but if Afonso would reconsider at his leisure, and if found that able to spare short time after wedding, perhaps he and Papa could take trip into Spain and look at those horses Uncle Pedro had been talking about. After pause to reconsider at his leisure, Afonso thumped Papa very hard on shoulder, shouted you-cunning-old-devil-you, both roared with laughter, both kissed me, both went off in direction of stables. Was left to assume Maria and Jorge's honeymoon now taken care of; decided that Papa cunning-old-devil-you.

Dinner party in honour of Papa and Mama; dinner perfect, was pleased to hear guest on Papa's right telling him that only old type of servant now willing to cook on old type of stove.

Monday August 14th.

Papa and Mama back to Lisbon, Mama with two of my cookery books.

Thursday August 17th.

Drew sketches, set carpenter to work on cupboards for kitchen; drove in Land Rover to village to give measurements for pink marble for working surfaces. Bought pink-and-white checked cotton material to make into kitchen curtains. Sent telegram to Philippa for wedding day.

Letter from Jinny, no mention of new Peer but said was bringing out dog for herself, would I like one? Wrote to say yes. Later, asked by Afonso what kind of dog, said I didn't know; he said was it actually possible that I had ordered dog without knowing what breed? Said yes, actually possible.

Monday August 21st.

Packed for Lisbon. Walked round house on frequent tours of inspection, changed beds round in two bedrooms, rearranged ornaments, decided house looking very nice indeed.

Postcard from Philippa written during halt on way to Scotland for honeymoon, very excited, said Francis's father came to wedding, grudgingly offered job a miserable salary; when about to leave for honeymoon, post bought bolt-from-blue offer from rival firm, honeymoon put off for few hours and Francis rushed to London for interview, got job, salary not astronomical but riches compared with Father's; Father furious, Francis refused to say which job would take; when arrived at Aviemore would talk over quietly and decide which. Oh incidentally, my mother at wedding, sent her love.

Tuesday, August 22nd.

Left Reinaldo for Lisbon and wedding. Afonso turned car north instead of south, told me surprise for me, going to show me little bit of country. Bit of country turned out to be Penamacor and Monsanto, back by way of Castelo Branco, where stayed night with Afonso's cousins; next day to Lisbon.

Thursday August 24th.

House temporarily cleared of all except family, in order to accommodate Jorge's mother, father, two sisters and four brothers; Jorge himself billeted at Aunt Isabel's, all due to arrive tomorrow. Bridesmaids coming and going, Senhora Dona Beatriz said head whirling, so much, too much to do.

Mama and Papa said would be so pleased if I would let them give me a dress for wedding. Said very kind, but surely too late to have one made, and Lisbon not as far as I knew well stocked with ready-mades. Mama said plenty of time to make, as her dressmaker, undoubtedly best in Lisbon, had put aside all other commitments for period of wedding in order to concentrate on needs of Mama and family. Set out at 11.30, had wonderful time in elegant shop choosing dress material, home to lunch; dressmaker summoned in afternoon, dress chosen with Afonso's so-called assistance.

Friday August 25th.

Large dinner party for Jorge's family; two very long tables in dining room, one for young, one for old; myself head of young table, Afonso at other end looking fatherly. Vasco home and happy, as Jorge's two sisters, though shy to point of dumbness, extremely pretty; younger sister unable to use tongue but amazingly expert with long black eyelashes.

Dinner very long; high peak of ceremony, everyone including self very smart, Mama and Jorge's mother a-twinkle with jewels which, as not presented by Uncle Feliciano, probably real. Short speech from Papa; long and confused one from Jorge's father, owing to *(a)* long succession of wines, *(b)* frequent promptings from wife and *(c)* naturally shy disposition like daughters. Speech included public acknowledgment of kindness of Afonso and self in lending Reinaldo for honeymoon; Afonso's expression seen to brighten as speaker added honeymoon unfortunately limited to two weeks, owing to bridegroom's commitments in Oporto. After dinner, party greatly enlarged by arrival of outer circle of relations; dancing in drawing room under eye of Senhora Dona Beatriz and colleague in charge of Jorge's two sisters, very difficult task, as Vasco vanished with one sister and José, retrieved from Navy for period of wedding, carried off the other, where to nobody knew and only Senhora Dona Beatriz and colleague cared. Afonso danced, I danced; he said how time flew, here we were, so short a time after own wedding, already growing out of young set, did I feel old hag? Said no; added that good thing Mother not at this gathering, or would go crazy trying to sort everybody out.

Saturday August 26th.

Small dinner party for Jorge's close relations; reception afterwards for older people, mostly relations and friends in Lisbon for wedding.

Wednesday August 30th.

To dressmaker for final fitting of own dress and to see Maria's and bridesmaids'. Maria's a dream, parchment brocade, very simple but simply lovely. Thought that Maria, in it, looked like nun once thought of becoming, changed my mind about blondes making most picturesque brides, as nothing able to rival beauty of Maria's dark curls piled up under bridal veil. Dressmaker, tottery but authoritative old harridan, surveyed effect and said Maria image of Mama on wedding day; this quite probable if one could imagine Mama young and slender.

Not much impressed by bridesmaids, six in number: Ana and Valeria, Jorge's two sisters, so far so good, but remaining two great blot on picture, couldn't imagine why Maria had included them, until remembered Clara Cornhill.

Thursday August 31st.

Wedding rehearsal, meant to be only for principals, but Church half full, told Afonso I felt people unconnected with ceremony should have stayed away; Afonso pointed out that he and I unconnected with ceremony. After rehearsal, back to house, which today open to receive anybody who cared to look in; running buffet in charge of wedding caterer. Asked Afonso what all this likely to cost, he said wasn't going to cost him a cent and for this reason enjoying it very much, hoped I was too.

Saturday September 2nd.

Wedding day. Got up early, Afonso stayed in bed; asked him why, when day promised excitement of any kind, he invariably refused to get up? He said conserving his energy, having discovered as child that if got up early, by time day's excitement arrived, own excitement abated, not to say evaporated.

Message from Mama, wanted to see me; went to her room, she said please go and talk to Maria, Maria crying, nobody able to console. Went to Maria's room, found Senhora Dona Beatriz there, she for once glad to see me, left me to cope. Maria in bed, all white nightdress with ruffles and pale pink sheets and crumpled handkerchief; discovered after probing that trouble was couldn't face leaving Papa, Mama, self and Afonso, José, Vasco, Alberto, Ana and Valeria, also Duarte, Luiz and Francisco; loved Jorge, but how to be happy away from own family? On one side so many loved ones, on other side only Jorge. Sat on bed, turned on record about the Bible's instructions to wives to leave all and cleave unto husbands; in own case, think how difficult, not case of leaving large and united family who could go on cleaving to one another, but leaving widowed mother all alone and going much farther than Maria was going, but Afonso now my duty, my life; was about to add my love, but thought it overdone. Told Maria instead that could now begin to pass on to her own family all the happiness she had had in her life; exhorted her to think of Mama and how Mama had left her home, wherever it was, and with Papa founded this splendid family, all so happy and united. Word united not good choice, taps turned on again. Said girls couldn't cling to outworn girlhood, but had to assume with pride and love mantle of womanhood. Thought this definitely overdone, but pleased to see Maria impressed, so went on to say that she in her turn would be able to reassure her sisters of joy and privilege of marriage, to say nothing of fun; added in sudden burst of candour that physical aspects of marriage not often enough placed under heading of fun, but in my view ought to be. Clear that this entirely novel idea to

Maria, she said that was wifely duty. I said all that old potato about submitting meekly was, well, it was so much old potato; male and female created He them, and a jolly good idea it was, and they could keep all that claptrap about children being born in original sin, because mine would all be born in love and laughter and I hope hers would be too, very hard on Jorge if not, and what would he think if he knew she was sitting in bed snuffling instead of leaping into her bridal dress and rushing to Church to swear to hold him until death did them part? Had satisfaction of seeing Maria out of bed, on way to bath; she said don't go away, such a lot to ask you. Stayed with her and answered it, then went back to Afonso. He said had I felt on my wedding morning that making a terrible mistake? Said no, only felt that after marriage.

Drove with Afonso to Church, rather late but to great surprise scarcely anybody inside; Afonso explained that custom in Portugal for guests to wait outside, if wanted to, to get good view of bride's arrival. Thought this mean trick, as considered every bride's prerogative to arrive at packed Church, breathless hush, screwed-round heads, and slow and dignified procession up aisle, instead of as in this case bridal procession followed by rush of guests making way to seats. Nuptial Mass. At end, pause to allow ex-royalty to depart with dignity, then general rush after bride and groom; at door, students from Coimbra University spread cloaks for bride to walk on. Back to house for reception, food superlative, asked Afonso if he knew how much per head caterers charged, he said didn't know and didn't care, and wished I didn't always try to turn feasts into figures.

When bride and bridegroom left, thought guests would leave too, but found most stayed on, young dancing, old eating and drinking. At midnight, first signs that wedding over; Mama and Papa stood in hall to say goodbye to one and all. Mama and I agreed that lovely wedding. Mama said my own just as nice.

Monday September 4th.

Signs of wedding obliterated: Jorge's relations vanished, furniture back in place, house as usual. Short message sent back by Jorge and Maria in station waggon, lent for luggage to Reinaldo: very happy, very grateful for lovely wedding, Reinaldo looking its best. Afonso said this obviously effect of honeymoon, as Reinaldo looking dry and dusty. Added that Papa would like to leave for Spain day after tomorrow if this suited me, added that not like Papa to hold up itinerary in order to find out what suited member of younger generation, sign of great respect for me. I said Papa and Afonso could go when they liked; self planning to have delirious time in Lisbon, shopping with Mama.

Tuesday September 5th.

Letter from Jinny, hoping wedding would go off without hitch, looking forward to seeing me again but not sure when, as tied up with American relations.

José back to Navy. Vasco to Florence, Mama says to look at pictures. Vasco confides that really to renew contact with lovely Italian, unfortunately broken for period of wedding; added that so nice to have me in family, as I understood these things. Told him I didn't understand these things at all, and considered him least satisfactory of all brothers-in-law. He kissed me with affection, said Afonso lucky man, hoped he would find someone like me; informed him he wouldn't find anybody like me in the places he was looking.

Wednesday September 6th.

Papa and Afonso left after breakfast in Afonso's car, Afonso driving, trying to look distraught at parting from me, but with horse expression am now beginning to recognize. Next few hours difficult, as longed to be with him, beside him, driving along with his hand in mine except when required for gears. Felt I should fight this clinging-wife attitude; fought it; lost fight.

Alberto to Paris with party of Coimbra fellow-students; large seeing-off party at station preceded by dinner at restaurant with Uncle Pedro, Alberto's godfather, as host.

Thursday September 7th.

Didn't feel well, stayed in bed, Mama came in, said over-tired after wedding. Got up for lunch; after lunch, Ana and Valeria departed with, naturally, Senhora Dona Beatriz, to stay with Jorge's sisters in Oporto. Duration of visit, one month. Luggage: five trunks, seven suitcases, two pairs water skis, large picnic hamper (present to Jorge's mother), fishing rod (present to Jorge's father).

Friday September 8th.

Francisco and Luiz to England to spend short time with English friends before returning to English school. Mama said how sad to have empty house; she and I must amuse ourselves until return of men. Began with dinner at restaurant with Uncle Feliciano and distant cousin Joao, afterwards to cinema.

Saturday September 9th.

Woke early, very sick; Mama said not wise to have eaten clams for dinner, must stay in bed until lunch time. Longed for Afonso. Large party for dinner, all family. Telephone call from Papa to say home day after tomorrow; Afonso also on line, said sad fact didn't enjoy jaunts as much as before marriage.

Monday September 11th.

Due to go shopping before lunch with Mama, but sent message saying would rather not, as upset by something eaten at dinner. Mama came to room, said would send in light breakfast, said didn't want light breakfast, rather eat nothing until lunch; lovely dinner, but feeling deathly sick, probably ate too much. Mama said no, thought hadn't eaten too much, she very experienced in these matters, advised letting her ask doctor to come and see me as in her view indisposition no connection with food. Sat bolt upright in bed, stared at her, said what, you mean a *baby* ? and was very sick. Recovering, said of course if so, very glad, only spoke in that tone from shock. Mama said good idea to see doctor, would call him; I said might as well know the worst, added didn't mean worst, simply figure of speech. Doctor came, diagnosis definite: baby in March. Mama gentle tears, me cascade; apologised, said pure nerves, very glad about baby, hoped would be as good a mother as my Mother and Mama. Mama said what wonderful news for Afonso, his birthday in March, wouldn't it be coincidence? Afonso and Papa home just before dinner. By arrangement with Mama, news to be broken to Papa later, and by self to Afonso in own room after dinner. Thought, when in own room after dinner, of how to break news, came out of reverie to hear Afonso, brushing teeth in bathroom, say he supposed Mama and I had spent last few days in shops. Said yes, and I had got something for his birthday. He said rather early for birthday present, but what was it? I said little colt or perhaps little filly, too early to say. Afonso went on brushing teeth. Brushing slowed, stopped, toothbrush fell into basin, Afonso swallowed large quantity of toothpaste, turned and stared at me through open doorway, mouth agape. Asked me what I had said? Asked him if he could teach me how to whinny, and would he please wipe foam off lips, news stupendous, but not as stupendous as all that. Handed him towel, found self enfolded in embrace, Afonso murmuring incoherently My wife My wife. I said in present circumstances, this very reassuring. Happy interlude, but bad night owing to Afonso turning on light every half hour to see if I was all right. Got very tired of this, urged him to go to sleep. At 3 a.m. lost last vestige of patience; when he said tenderly for twentieth time How do you feel?, I shouted at top of voice I FEEL PREGNANT!

Part 3

Wednesday, September 13th

Financial crisis owing to discovery by Afonso that Bank account overdrawn; nothing to do with gas stove, which paid for by estate; due, Afonso said, to my extravagance and general inability to Manage. Told him that my extravagance consisted of buying a few metres of inexpensive material to be made up into Maternity wear until my Mother could send out from England; other expenditure his, with exception of dry stores ordered by me from Lisbon as instructed by him. Argument ended by decision to sit down and draw up Budget. Did so. Budget showed that salary sufficient only for basic needs; overdrawn state shown to be caused by fact that I had paid bills hitherto passed by Afonso to estate. I said wanted salary large enough to live on; Afonso said present salary very generous; I pointed out that Budget didn't even stretch to clothing family, him or me or coming child; proposed showing Budget to Papa. Afonso said no, had always found salary adequate and saw no reason for asking for increase. I said salary had never been adequate; had been in nature of allowance, adequate only be-

139

cause Afonso had charged most of his expenses to estate; now things different, and essential for us to get living wage and live on it; any other course simply cadging. Added that what was needed was meeting of himself, self, Papa and Mama to discuss sensibly and clearly fair wage, after which presents and favours better reduced to minimum and confined to festive occasions. Budget, after more argument, drawn up again on more realistic lines and carried by Afonso to Papa's study. Mama and I called to meeting, money openly and honestly discussed, list at my request drawn up of exactly what chargeable to estate and what not; Papa said all his fault this step not taken earlier; Afonso said no, his fault for drifting; Mama said her fault for not having spoken to me at first opportunity about household expenses. Final agreement: cook, housemaid, parlourmaid, laundress and gardener our servants; no others to be used; if called upon for help on special occasions, to be paid by us and not by estate. Journeys by Land Rover strictly on estate business to be paid by estate funds, all other journeys our own expense. Mama pointed out that this would limit our visits to Lisbon, which not good thing; Papa said was sure that I would give them pleasure of frequent visits and make saving in other directions. Meeting interesting, as self only one present who accustomed to face fact that money useful commodity but liable to come to end, leaving no more available anywhere. Felt that Afonso, with Papa and Mama solidly behind him, constitutionally unable to view finances seriously, but self determined to keep within salary and achieve feeling of independence, even if illusory.

Thursday September 14th.

Drove back to Reinaldo with Afonso; Mama and Papa following, as Mama in need of rest after wedding. Afonso drove at infuriatingly slow pace, due to anxiety about dislodging baby. Got to Reinaldo to find staff assembled, news of pregnancy obviously spread, though nobody knows how; congratulations all round. Mama and Papa arrived, car followed by station waggon; Mama said had brought a few stores with her, to help out. Stores to help out: tea, coffee, sugar, butter, tinned hams, sacks of rice, sacks of dried beans, several boxes of crystallised fruit (Papa likes), several boxes peppermint creams (I like), unlimited quantity of coffee creams (Afonso likes). Dinner, planned and prepared by cook, very good; felt that in this direction at least, great improvement effected since marriage.

Peaceful weekend, Sunday notable for usual unusual turnout of one and all for Mass, always to be observed when Papa and Mama here. Next day Afonso back at work, he and Papa out most of day; self and Mama relaxed, but Mama full of plans for *(a)* Papa's birthday in November *(b)* Valeria's birthday in December *(c)* Christmas *(d)* Mama's birthday in January *(e)* Afonso's birthday and baby's birthday in March. In middle of planning, she said why didn't I ask my Mother to come out for Christmas and stay on until birth of baby? I said had occurred to me, but hadn't proposed it as quite certain

Mother would think period far too long. Mama said not long at all, must write and ask her. Afonso, told of this, said Mother would probably like to come out in November for weekend of horse fair; told him my mother one person who could be relied on to be more interested in me than in horses.

While Afonso in bath, telephone call for Papa; heard my name, said I hoped nothing wrong. Papa said no, no, no, simply to say that parcels for me had arrived at Lisbon post office and as not delivered until called for, had instructed maid to go and fetch. After slight pause, asked me what I had had sent out from England. Said had asked my mother to send me material for cushions and curtains. Papa said had I asked her to write clearly *Old Clothing Only?* Said no. Papa said this great pity. Asked why. He said all parcels containing new clothing opened and assessed for duty. I said well, tell them to open and assess and I would pay duty. Papa said hesitatingly that as matter of fact, parcels already opened and assessed; duty somewhat heavy. Asked him how heavy. He said that maid had telephoned for instructions, as duty very heavy. Asked how heavy. After pause, during which braced myself, heard Papa say that as matter of fact, duty on both parcels amounted to sum of two *contos* or two thousand escudos. Did swift exchange sum, said instantly that mistake on part of post office; two *contos* equal to about twenty-five pounds in English money, which more than material likely to have cost. Papa said yes, pity not to have put *Old Clothing Only* but too late now, maid instructed to pay duty so all well. Thanked him, said I would give him cheque in repayment; wondered where I would get it without bringing new, precious Budget crashing down in ruins. Papa said no, no, no, he would most certainly pay duty. Tried to say no, I would, found to my horror that about to howl so said nothing; Papa took hand, patted, said this little secret between himself and myself, no need to mention to Afonso, only too happy to do this little thing for me. Said thank you, went to bedroom, howled; decided would tell Afonso but not Mother.

Wednesday September 20th.

Papa and Mama back to Lisbon.

Thursday September 21st.

Long and joyful letter from Mother in answer to mine telling her of pregnancy; said had at once rushed to telephone to tell Uncle George and Aunt Freda; Uncle George said very pleased, but fuss and excitement unnecessary as no doubt frequent future occasions for similar rejoicing. Mother said was of course coming out in March for event, please write and tell her what to bring out with her, was going up to Town next week and would look at Maternity wear. Afonso came back to lunch with news that property nearest to ours now changed hands, would I write letter asking newcomers to dine. Wrote letter, watched bearer, on half-wild horse, vanish across-country towards neighbouring Quinta. Reply stated very grateful, glad to dine tomorrow.

Friday September 22nd.

New neighbours to dinner; names Gustavo and Elisa Pinto, married just before Afonso and self; he rather stocky, immensely strong-looking; she little wisp with big black eyes; like self, pregnant, baby expected second week in March, going to have it in house of her parents in Tomar. She said Gustavo busy outside, she coping with house, which bought lock stock and barrel from previous owners and not in good state; servants had been taken over with house, but were now leaving one by one on seeing that new owners more concerned with cleanliness and order than previous ones. Offered to go over next day and help her; she said hadn't liked to suggest it but would be very grateful.

Saturday September 23rd.

Drove over to Pintos, found Elisa in midst of complete chaos: house very old, rabbit warren of rooms, but solid and comfortable once hideous ornaments and decorations got rid of. Decided to take one room at a time, started on drawing room; sent for empty packing cases and put into it all horrors: china cocks, china rabbits, china pigs, innumerable examples of fretwork and antimacassars embroidered with scenes from Passion. Also, on walls, several pictures, very holy, very gory, very depressing not to say terrifying for forthcoming baby. Saw that Elisa unwilling to take down; took it upon myself to do so, handing them to maids and saying that the Senhora had even holier pictures she wished to put up in their place. Elisa pink with gratitude, but no comment. When packing case at last removed, room almost bare, but liveable-in; another maid gave notice, Elisa unmoved as said her mother sending replacements from Tomar. As Gustavo away for day, drove Elisa back to lunch at Reinaldo, then back to clear rest of rooms. Halt for tea; by evening, adjacent shed full of discards and house ready for setting-out of Elisa's treasures. Dinner at Reinaldo with Gustavo and Elisa; Afonso said when gone that nice for me to have friend like Elisa, so different from Jinny Freitas.

Monday September 25th.

Letter from Jinny: had intended to come out with dogs before end of month, but impossible as no ship before October 7th, could I meet? If not, she and Manuel would bring dog over to Reinaldo. Asked Afonso if possible to go to Lisbon for weekend October 7*th*; he said no use asking him, deciding factor how much in petrol fund.

Tuesday September 26th.

Out all day watching grape-picking. Harvest said to be not-good. Went down to Wine Lodge with Afonso after dinner to watch treading; not picturesque, as wine lodge very small, treading tank very small, treading done in rather gloomy silence by three rather gloomy men, but liked sitting in semi-darkness on upturned barrel under lantern hung from beams, men's faces swarthy, glistening with sweat, sound of treading rhythmic not to say hypnotic. Afonso surprised at my unwillingness to leave, said had understood me to say had seen same thing only bigger and better in France; I said yes, but then had no sense of ownership.

Friday September 29th.

Letter from Mother, said very grateful for invitation to come out for Christmas and stay on for baby, longed to accept but quite impossible; for one thing, dogs, who would look after? and garden, who would tend? and Spring planting, who would do? also Spring cleaning, who would supervise? Had also been giving lessons on organ to quite incompetent organist of Catholic Church, how to abandon? Also now President of Women's Institute, how to miss so many monthly meetings? Quite out of question, especially as also went along of an evening to read to poor old Mrs. Nunn, so ill now, almost ninety, little cottage of hers so damp, so cheerless; please forgive her for putting all these things before visit to me, but really impossible to manage so prolonged a visit from home; would love to come out in March for baby, nothing would keep her from me at that time, was writing to Afonso's mother to thank her for kind invitation, but impossible accept.

Saturday September 30th.

Letter from Uncle George. Had just returned home after dropping in to see Mother. Found her red about the eyes, learned had just posted letter to me saying impossible to come out from Christmas to March. Impossible Uncle George's foot. Dogs could be left with Aunt Freda, she only too glad as very lonely since poor old Ringer put away last month. Spring planting would be arranged by himself as always, Mother didn't know first thing about it, never had. Spring cleaning nothing but nervous, not to say pathological manifestation, house clean as whistle, Spring cleaning his foot. Organist and W.I. disposed of in short sharp phrase. Old Mrs. Nunn deaf as post, so obviously waste of time to read to her, simply lonely, needed company, appeal launched for Television set, subscription list headed by himself, wouldn't hear the programmes, which no loss, but plenty to look at. With regard to fare, had taken care of that but not by air as if he knew anything, by time Mother ready to leave, would have collected enough junk to sink ship; hoped all well with me, nice to hear about baby but no need to give too many repeat performances. Read letter twice, cried, wrote to say thank you.

Monday October 2nd.

Dinner with Gustavo and Elisa; also her father and mother, down from Tomar on visit. After dinner, men talked about bulls and horses, women inspected baby clothes brought by Elisa's mother; I said how nice, but felt future baby going to be clothed like Eskimo if not totally smothered.

Tuesday October 3rd.

Rang up Mama, asked if Afonso and self could come down for weekend. She said delighted, would I like to see doctor while there? Said no.

Friday October 6th.

Drove with Afonso to Lisbon; arrived just before dinner, Mama said little family party assembled to meet us, sat down to dinner twenty-six strong. Learned afterwards from Aunt Isabel that daughter Ana pregnant, fourth child on way; nearly said Oh bad luck but stopped in time and offered congratulations.

Saturday October 7th.

To lunch with Uncle Feliciano at restaurant; enjoyed it in spite of conviction that would have to pay for it; Uncle Feliciano no doubt crooked, but charming, and in my view better-informed than all rest of brothers put together. On way out, ran into Manuel Freitas who said how nice, ship due five o'clock, meet us there. Went to meet ship, Jinny on deck looking last word in cool elegance. Manuel went on board, brought Jinny ashore, no sign of dogs. Greeted Jinny, was about to ask where dog, and what sort, when man appeared leading two beautiful Great Dane pups. I said Oh how lovely, Afonso said was that Jinny's idea of a house dog? Jinny said if he hadn't wanted Great Dane, had had plenty of time to say so, these were highly bred and as gentle as lambs. Afonso said yes, and as big as elephants, did she realise that our house was modest residence, not palace like hers ? She said just like him to spoil everything, how I managed to live with him was more than she could see. I said dog lovely, didn't ask how much as felt Afonso not able to take more shocks. After long formalities concerning entry of dogs into country, led ours, name of Viking, to car, where with great difficulty accommodated between Afonso and self. Arrived at house, dog lolloped into hall, slipped, recovered, lurched against valuable jar, which rescued by Afonso. Papa came into hall, Viking gave joyous bark and joyous bound, horrid picture of Papa sitting on bottom stair having face licked; rescued by Afonso. Mama came into hall, dog gave joyous bark, about to give joyous bound when Afonso circumvented; Afonso and dog slithered, lost footing, Afonso lost dog. Dog vanished upstairs, Papa said better send chauffeur up and have dog taken to garage for time being. Afonso said bitterly that Jinny Freitas distorted sense of humour. Dinner with Manuel and Jinny; Afonso and Manuel talked about bulls and horses, Jinny told me about London shops. She said had brought me rather alluring Maternity dress; asked her how she knew about baby, she said Afonso had told a man who told a man who told Manuel.

Sunday October 8th.

Left Lisbon in late afternoon, got home after uncomfortable journey with dog wedged between Afonso and self. Also in car, parcels containing chair and curtain material.

Wednesday October 11th.

Letter from Mother; of course I had had Uncle George's letter? Aunt Freda said so much better not to argue with him, quite violent when thwarted; for this reason, as well of course for pleasure of being with me, had decided to accept his kind offer of keeping eye on things in her absence. Had been up to Town and put name on waiting list of ship sailing for Lisbon on December 16th, travel agent said would not know for some time whether berth available or not, would I let her know what to bring out? Wrote off to her at once, said lovely to see her, please bring tea, toothpaste, tinned baked beans, mango chutney, mustard pickles, packets of tissues, curry paste, packets dried herbs, English biscuits, large bottles malted milk.

Chair covers cut out. Drove into village in Land Rover, taking sofa to man who mends springs. Viking beginning to walk round room without knocking over everything in path.

Sunday October 15th.

Rain. Afonso said too early, won't last.

Wednesday October 18th.

Still raining. Ground outside house sea of mud, Viking's paw-marks, size of abominable snowman's, all over verandah floor.

Friday October 20th.

Weather fine but rather cold; Maternity dresses being made up but wish I had bought warmer material. Viking in disgrace, as found and chewed new boots bought by Afonso to wear at forthcoming horse fair at Golegã on November 11th. Elisa and Gustavo, back from visit to parents in Tomar, to dinner; Jinny and Manuel also present; this first meeting between Jinny and Elisa but decided mistake to try and mix them; Afonso said afterwards like chalk and cheese.

Monday October 23rd.

Incredible letter from Mama, essence of sweetness but containing news that her cook had left after serious disagreement with one of housemaids, new cook urgently needed, but Mama had some time ago promised that if ever cook needed, post would be offered to Joséfina; would I please send her? So sorry to take her away from me, but always plentiful supply of girls at Reinaldo, so had no fear of leaving me without cook. Read letter several times, unable to believe eyes, remained in state of seethe until lunch time, then waited until Afonso nearly finished delicious meal before telling him that his mother stealing our cook. Gave letter to him to read, was furious to see him still calm and unmoved at end; he said yes, quite true that inexhaustible labour fund to draw on here, and his mother had always engaged her maids from those working at Reinaldo; these always eager to get to Lisbon to earn more money and see more life. I said this system perfectly in order before my advent, but had Afonso any idea how many hours I had spent with Joséfina in kitchen, teaching her how to cook something besides chicken-with-rice-and-peppers? He said any girl with average intelligence could pick up cooking hints. When able to

speak, said was glad to know how much he appreciated superlative meals lately served to him. He said groom, Alfredo, had
daughter who only too glad to come and cook, and they could
live in the little house just inside wall, couldn't remember
girl's name but would speak to Alfredo this afternoon. I said
had no intention of training girls only to have them whisked
away by his mother. He said his mother running very large
establishment, more important for her to have good cook than
for us, living so quietly in country; added that Joséfina's own
wishes to be considered, not fair to prevent her from going to
bigger and better job. Told him that would for moment take on
daughter of Alfredo, but refused absolutely to train as cooks
any more Reinaldo girls, was going to see Elisa this afternoon
and ask her to get me cook from Tomar. Afonso said that after all Mama's kindness, surprised at my begrudging her first
request ever made to me. I said not question of begrudging,
this a question of ethics, and his mother well aware that ser-
vant-snatching very unethical indeed. After lunch, went into
kitchen, told Joséfina that had had letter, was about to say from
whom, when Joséfina in polite but eager manner said that the
Lady Mother had always promised to take her to Lisbon if
cook needed; did Lady Mother say when she was to go? I said
no, but as far as I was concerned, the sooner the better. Drove
to Elisa's, by this time cool enough to admit that perhaps in
this case previous promise to Joséfina justification for taking
her away from me, but quite determined not to give up any
more trained cooks. Gave Elisa no details, merely asked her if

could get me cook from Tomar; she said would telephone to her mother. Stayed to tea, as two other neighbours coming and didn't want to appear not-anxious to meet them; when arrived, conversation entirely of forthcoming horse fair; heard myself accepting invitation to join large party there, hoped Afonso would approve. Told him at dinner, found he didn't approve.

Wednesday October 25th.

Joséfina came to say goodbye and collect wages. Offered transport to station, Joséfina said cousin coming to fetch her. Cousin, male, arrived on donkey, leading second donkey on which Joséfina and suitcase mounted and departed. Alfredo's daughter reported to be waiting for me in kitchen; went to talk to her, found her large, strong, handsome girl full of self-confidence; told her that this temporary post, as engaging cook from Tomar; slight cloud on listener's face vanished when learned that house for self and father not affected by this. Lunch, chicken-with-rice-and-peppers; dinner vegetable soup, baked fish, tasteless mutton, boiled potatoes, caramel custard. Afonso, about to complain, decided not to.

Friday October 27th.

Rain. Afonso says too early for winter rains, will pass.

Still raining. Viking's head now on level with plates in dining room, food removed from plates. Carpenter sent for, given orders to make large kennel.

Friday November 3rd.

Still raining. Brief sunny intervals during which attempts made to dry clothes. Interrupted carpenter in making of kennel, told him to make clothes pulley to fix in kitchen. Carpenter never having heard of pulley, drew sketch for him and went through motions of pulling pulley up and down. Carpenter left to get more wood. Telephone call from Jinny, could we dine tomorrow night? Said dinner difficult as Afonso not back from Golegã, where going on business connected with horse fair; arranged to go to lunch instead, without Afonso. Telephone call from Elisa, her mother interviewing cooks, hoped to send me one before middle of month; if not, without fail before end.

Saturday November 4th.

Lunch with Jinny. Took Viking to allow him to play with his brother. Heavy, unceasing rain; Jinny said Portuguese climate very much overrated, fiction kept up by travel agents that charming all year round, when in actual fact very windy in summer and very wet in winter, only endurable by reason of brief but perfect Spring and Autumn. Asked if I would go to horse fair with her; said sorry, had already promised to join party, was looking forward to going, as heard nothing but horse fair for weeks. Jinny said of interest only to local farmers, horse-breeders and tourists, she herself would never go near it, but Manuel insisted on token interest in local life. Took me up to her room and showed me purchases made while in England; was presented with light wool Maternity suit. Lunched in dining room before enormous wood fire; two dogs sat in front of it and steamed.

Telephone call from Elisa: cook arriving from Tomar on 20th. Letter from Mama; she and Papa coming up to horse fair, would like to stay night with us but would have to leave after lunch on Sunday, as dining out in Lisbon; also, Papa's birthday on Saturday 18th, if Afonso and I could come down, make nice little family party. No mention of Joséfina, but Afonso said at lunch that rumours going round estate to effect that Lisbon turning her head, behaviour not up to standard; I said that was willing to bet that in case of Joséfina, Mama would be prepared to turn blind eye, as cooks like Joséfina hard to come by. Afonso said not hard at all, simply matter of training, and how long was he going to be given food like this, as digestion beginning to suffer. I said digestion would have to suffer until 20th, when new cook arrived.

Wednesday November 8th.

Sofa and chair covers ready but no sign of sofa, still with man in village for mending. Third message sent, third reassuring message received; sofa practically on way. Drove to village, found sofa untouched, gave man remarkably fluent piece of mind, waited until he had embarked on repair work. Went back to sounds of lamentation: carpenter had brought ladder to fix hook in ceiling of kitchen to attach pulley, ladder gave way, carpenter fell on to fish stew on clay stove, now being treated for fish scalds. Produced my very Red-Cross-looking medicine case, parting gift from Aunt Mary, bought by her during War, never used. Opened it with difficulty, found entire contents unusable owing to leakage or seepage of bottle of iodine; threw it away and told cook to go on applying goose grease to scalds.

Mama and Papa for night after wettest horse fair in local annals. Howling wind, rain beating down in torrents, continued non-stop throughout day; stands almost useless, not being built to withstand tropical storms. Men dripping, grooms dripping, horses dripping, most of unfortunate sightseers dripping. Mama and Papa remained in car until time to drive to Reinaldo. Elisa apologetic for having suggested my joining her friends, who nowhere to be seen; this very awkward, as had depended on them for lunch. Joined by Elisa's mother and father who had driven down from Tomar; ate remnants of their picnic lunch; mother said good news for me, promising cook engaged, name of Dulcelinda, only drawback not available until end of month. Said very grateful, could manage with present cook until arrival of Dulcelinda. Occasional wet glimpses of Afonso, who told me to go home with Mama and Papa. Got home and settled down in front of living room fire, no sign of Afonso, Viking also missing; both appeared about nine-thirty, both mud-covered. Dinner terrible, conversation everything but food. After dinner Mama, with me on sofa, said in gentle but vexed tone that Joséfina behaving badly, even talked of leaving and going to more highly-paid job; such a thing had never happened before with any girl from Reinaldo, perhaps I had spoiled Joséfina just a little. I said didn't spoil servants. Mama said of course didn't suggest such a thing, merely meant to say that people unused to dealing with Portuguese servants failed to understand that firmness necessary as well as kindness; indulgence mistaken for weakness, and advantage taken; in case of Joséfina, myself too young to impose kind of discipline needed; for this, experience necessary, especially experience with servants. Took this to mean that as in England grubbed along with daily maid, couldn't be expected to cope with staff. Counted ten, said in tone of remarkable forbearance that perhaps Joséfina essentially country type who unable to withstand temptations of big city; added that if Joséfina not satisfactory, perhaps my present cook more suitable? free to go at end of month. Pause, Mama hopeful of further details, self determined not to supply. Mama said had I found another girl on estate? Said no, girls on estate very good, very sweet, very good house workers but not good cook material, so had decided to go farther afield. Mama said staff for Reinaldo house never before recruited from outside, didn't I think difficult for outsider to settle here? Said only time would show. Mama said perhaps ought to have talked to Papa before bringing in girl from outside; I said didn't think Papa at all interested in cook question. Papa and Afonso came in from verandah, thought Mama was going to ask him about cook, but prevented by Afonso, who anxious to demonstrate Viking's new trick. Viking asked to give English handshake; gave English handshake. In bed, told Afonso about exchange with Mama, waited for him to remind me of Mama's kindness and generosity, heard him say instead that she could have all our servants, just so long as she kept her hands off our cook, and self free to recruit them from anywhere I pleased just so long as I trained them and gave him decent food again. Embraced him passionately, lay with head on his shoulder explaining that liked his mother, but necessary to make early stand about servants. Spoke with reason and fluency until discovered Afonso fast asleep. Woke him up to ask if he had asked Papa about gas fridge; he said, among other things, no.

Sunday November 12th.

Asked Afonso on return of family from Mass whether had mentioned gas fridge to Papa; he said why this fuss about gas fridge with winter coming on? No fridge necessary until next summer, and very hard for Papa to be asked for one, as whatever he did for us, he felt bound in honour to do for other nine children. I said none of them at present, with possible exception of Maria, in need of gas fridge. Papa and Mama drove away, nothing said about gas fridge.

Wednesday November 15th.

Afonso out for day; was about to go out to lunch at Jinny's, when she rang up to say Elisa coming too, would I give her lift? Called for Elisa, impressed by fact that although rain cascading down, she could walk to car without getting feet muddy; determined to have front of Reinaldo house similarly paved. On way to Jinny's, Elisa said so difficult to accept invitation, as Gustavo much against asking her back; didn't like her, though liked Manuel. I said unwise to fall in with all views uttered by husband on wife's friends; in my view Jinny served useful purpose by open and uninhibited expression of opinion on subjects which I felt better ventilated than not. Elisa said didn't think Gustavo would agree with this. Arrived to find Jinny in light woollen slacks and black jersey, said how nice to see us without our husbands, nothing against Gustavo and Afonso but wished they wouldn't show so clearly how much they loathed her, would we like sherry or gin ? I said sherry, and thought Jinny very good-natured to work so hard trying to put Elisa at her ease; Elisa unresponsive until suddenly remembered, halfway through lunch, that one of her cousins had said had met Jinny at party in Lisbon. Jinny said which cousin? was it the one who'd run away with that Danish girl who'd run away from her husband? Obvious from Elisa's look of horror that this lapse entirely unknown to her; Jinny did best to repair damage by saying that probably only malicious rumour or odd coincidence of names. Elisa, recovering over coffee, said neighbour on other side of her had baby last night. Jinny said that made the fourth in four years, and if she had husband like that, would chain him outside bedroom door; had we heard about this painless childbirth? didn't want to dash our hopes, but her sister-in-law entirely taken in, was told that all she had to do was breathe and wouldn't feel a thing, breathed like anything and had ghastly time, must we really go? On way home, Elisa said perhaps Gustavo right about Jinny. I said perhaps he wasn't. Left it at that.

Saturday November 18th.

Up very early, left after breakfast for Lisbon. Stopped at shop to buy birthday present for Papa, looked at silk pyjamas, couldn't afford. Priced very nice wool sports shirts; couldn't afford. Afonso went over to handkerchief counter; I looked across road and saw gas fridges in window of shop opposite, went to look, went inside, heard Afonso's voice, saw him in doorway looking dangerous, went back to handkerchief shop, bought six, said very unoriginal present. On way to car, saw in shop window soft leather case which looked like wallet but which when opened proved to be eight photograph frames; said this very thing for Papa, we could fill the frames before presenting to him, pity not ten frames for ten children. Afonso pointed out had already bought present; I said would put handkerchiefs aside and give them as Christmas presents, so no money wasted. Bought wallet, with Mama's help filled frames with photographs and snaps of family and presented to Papa, who genuinely pleased. Had bath, changed into Jinny's Maternity dress, Mama admired, said tonight just quiet little family party. Not surprised, on entering drawing room before dinner, to find large concourse. Valeria, Ana, Afonso and self only young ones, all others Papa's generation or generation before or, judging by appearances, generation before that. Mama, in aside, told me Joséfina behaving much better.

Afonso back to Reinaldo, self at Mama's insistence left behind for extra day, as doctor unable see me before Monday, having been away. Telephone call from Elisa, new cook coming after all on 20th; asked her to keep her until my return.

Tuesday November 21st.

Back to Reinaldo, Dulcelinda installed: age about thirty-six, short, plump, massive arms and legs, dark face, loud voice, ready smile and general appearance of willingness to try hand at cooking for first time for foreigner.

Letter from Mother; still on ship's waiting list. Letter from Philippa, back in London, couldn't find decent flat so went to see old one, found it empty, interviewed landlady who at first suspicious but afterwards reassured, Francis finding work tedious, wishes he had gone on stage as had always wanted to do, only no encouragement from father.

Monday November 27th.

Elisa came to say Gustavo dissatisfied with their food, could I teach her how to make some of the things Gustavo had liked when at Reinaldo? Lent her Tante Marie, Mrs. Beeton and Fanny Farmer; on opening and looking, she said could read some English, but not oz and lb; also unable understand oven temperatures in Fahrenheit. Told her that conversion quite simple, you just subtracted 32 and took five-ninths of remainder; realised this not sinking in, so drew thermometer and marked Fahrenheit on one side and Centigrade on the other, work of art. Elisa, in dazed voice, said everything now quite clear, went away.

Letter from Mama: as Valeria's birthday on December 22nd, hoped Afonso and I would come down early for Christmas visit. Realised that tomorrow December, Christmas and arrival of Mother, then New Year, then in no time at all, baby. Couldn't believe it, went and looked at myself in glass, believed it.

Thursday December 7th.

Lunch party for twelve, women only, first try-out of Dulcelinda. Food a success, party only partial success owing to Jinny's unasked-for but freely given views on how to cow bull tendencies in husbands.

Tuesday December 12th.

Worried letter from Mother: had called in to see travel agents, still very low on waiting list, hope of berth fading, plenty available for Rio de Janeiro, Santos, Sao Paulo and Buenos Aires, but none for Lisbon. Thought of writing to advise her to book for Rio de Janeiro and at last moment say would only go to Lisbon, but felt useless to urge crooked course. Told Afonso Mother's passage not available, he said did I mean to tell him she had been sitting on a waiting list all this time? Said yes, had told him so. He said first he had heard of it, I couldn't have mentioned it or he would have told me to get in touch with Uncle Manuel, who old crony of Managing Director of had forgotten which Portuguese shipping firm, no connection with waiting lists. After much difficulty, Uncle Manuel located at Mama's house, where having lunch; told him over phone of desperate case of Mother, unable to get berth on ship. Uncle Manuel said was seeing his friend next week or week after, would arrange something. Pointed out that week after next too late, Uncle Manuel said was Christmas so near? how time flew! and rang off. Mama rang up later to say wished had known I was on phone, such wonderful news, Maria to have baby in early June, everybody delighted; would Afonso and I come down for Valeria's birthday and stay on over Christmas? Said would ask Afonso. Asked Afonso, he said no, too busy.

Thursday December 14th.

Letter from Mother, now no hope of passage, luggage far too heavy to think of flying, perhaps better to come out for New Year, when rush over. Asked Afonso what his Uncle Manuel had been doing. Uncle Manuel located at his office, said matter had quite slipped his mind, so sorry, would see about it at once and ring us during morning. Packed few things for Lisbon, felt restless, wrote letters, worried about Mother, no word from Uncle Manuel all day.

Friday December 15th.

Afonso telephoned to Uncle Manuel, learned away from Lisbon for day. Told Afonso what I thought of all his uncles, but didn't feel much better after it.

Saturday December 16th.

Uncle Manuel still away from Lisbon, not returning until after weekend.

Monday December 18th.

Pouring rain. Wrapped presents previously bought in Lisbon for Jinny and Elisa, gave order for them to be delivered on Christmas Day. Felt depressed about Mother, decided when reached Lisbon would send her telegram saying please reconsider air travel. Arrived late, owing to Afonso's over-attention to my condition and condition of roads. Uncle Manuel at house, asked him if any news from his shipping friend, he said what shipping friend? Told him. He said very unlike him to have let matter slip his mind, would go round and see him and ring me up. Didn't ring me up.

Tuesday December 19th.

Talked to Papa about sending telegram to Mother about air travel; Papa said pity hadn't asked Manuel to help in matter. Said had, but Uncle Manuel forgotten. Papa said Manuel very good very kind but very absent-minded, would go at once to see what could be done. Went, came back with Uncle Manuel and aged gentleman with hair like Chateaubriand; patted my hand, said would I give him details? Gave them, gentleman went away leaning on arm of Uncle Manuel. Lunch for eighteen young relations given by Uncle Feliciano, afterwards to cinema. Film not well chosen, mother dying but keeps news from daughter, daughter learns accidentally, flies to mother, mother gone. Howled throughout, Afonso said like sitting next to waterfall. Got home, Mama advised dinner in bed; had dinner in bed, fell asleep, was awakened by Afonso with telegram from Mother: phone call from travel agent, berth on ship arriving Lisbon December 23rd. Afonso said that no hope of her bringing any luggage, as in rush to catch boat would leave everything behind. Wrote letter of thanks to old gentleman, sent round by hand.

Friday December 22nd.

Dinner party for Valeria's birthday, dancing afterwards. Tried to be gay, but thinking of Mother's arrival on morrow and too confused to give attention to guests, who almost all friends of Valeria and unknown to me or to Afonso. Afonso said halfway through party that company too young for his liking, made him feel two hundred years old.

Cloudy, but no rain. Mother's ship said to be due 8.30 a.m. At eight, me up and dressed, Afonso still in bed. Threatened to go without him; he said never knew a ship that came in when it said it would, why didn't I relax? I said latest information was that ship almost alongside; he said that meant it was just entering mouth of Tagus. Said I would give him ten minutes. Ten minutes later, Afonso asleep. Went out, took his car and drove to docks. Arrived, saw ship long way away and proceeding at leisurely pace, impossible to see figures on deck. At 9.15, ship came to total stop. 9.30, began to draw nearer. At 10, distant row of figures on deck but impossible to identify. At 10.30, Afonso appeared in Papa's car, sent it away again, strolled over to me and pointed out Mother on deck. Waved madly, ship came alongside, saw Mother very smart in tan woollen dress, recognised it as one of Aunt Freda's. Told Afonso to give me passes obtained yesterday for going on board; Afonso, after search of pockets, announced regretfully that passes in pocket of suit not worn. Began to tell him what I thought of him, he said mustn't agitate myself on account of baby. Shouted to Mother that passes unfortunately left behind, Mother unable hear owing to noise of cranes. After interval, Mother seen coming down gangway, happy reunion, she said how well we looked, hoped no trouble with Customs, as had got disproportionate amount of luggage. Papa's car appeared with Papa and Mama, Papa took charge of luggage and Customs, then he and Mama drove away; station waggon drew up and loaded luggage; Mother and Afonso and I got into our car. Mother asked me in aside if approved of her outfit, I said very smart, she said so kind of Aunt Freda, who had lent her all the clothes she had bought for that cruise she was going on but didn't, owing to last-minute change of mind on part of Uncle George owing to ship's last-minute change of itinerary;

clothes now so useful, as silly to buy expensive things when so little use for them at cottage.

Sunday December 24th.

Pouring. Mother asked me if this weather unseasonal, I said no, went on until end of winter. Asked to unpack some of the heavy luggage, she said no, much better to wait until arrival at Reinaldo. General move to Church, Afonso making detour to take Mother and self to ours. Large dinner party with Mother as guest of honour, French spoken as known by most; Mother's rusty but adequate. At 11.30, departure to Midnight Mass. Home, sandwiches in drawing room and then brief Christmas greetings all round but no distribution of presents. Bed. Went to say goodnight to Mother, she said how many cooks here? I said one, trained by me, but numerous assistants. Mother said all this must cost staggering amount, hoped I was keeping things in proportion in my own home and not letting my housekeeping become extravagant, must live simply as at cottage. Said no use giving Afonso egg and lettuce. Interrupted by Afonso in dressing gown, said sorry to intrude on cosy chat but very late, would I please accompany him to our bedchamber. Did so.

Christmas Day.

House open all morning to constant stream of relations, friends and well-wishers: tea, coffee, sherry or champagne. Maid on duty to remove unending litter of Christmas wrappings from drawing room and hall. After presentation of modest gifts from Afonso and self, settled down happily in corner to inspect own haul: handbag from Mother, air-light suitcase from Papa, matching night case from Mama, larger matching case, fitted, combined gift of José, Vasco, Alberto, Maria, Ana, Valeria, Francisco and Luiz. Stockings, handkerchiefs, table-mats from uncles and aunts; from Uncle George, copy of newly-translated Bible; from Aunt Freda, Maternity smock. From Uncle Feliciano, diamond bracelet. Nothing from Afonso, searched among wrappings, nothing; he asked me what I was looking for, this? took small package from pocket; when opened, disclosed delicate little gold chain on which small gold locket. Locket, when opened, disclosed photograph of horse; this joke enjoyed by Afonso for rest of day. At lunch Mother, under not unreasonable assumption that this main meal of day, ate well, was appalled to learn from me later that that only light lunch, full-scale dinner tonight. Before dinner, summoned by maid to Mother's room, she said would I help her to do small piece of stitching, Aunt Freda's black dinner gown rather too décolleté, must be taken up at neck. I said not at all too décolleté; Mother said must allow her to be judge, couldn't dream of showing so much at her age. Needle threaded, exposed area reduced. Dinner long and formal, Mother when saying goodnight to me said so thankful to be going to Reinaldo tomorrow, as quite apart from seeing my home, found so many guests confusing; added that Mama had given her kind invitation to stay, Mother had said would be glad to come when self in Lisbon having baby.

Tuesday December 26th.

Packed, ready to go home. Papa and Mama made last-minute appeal to stay longer, Afonso said sorry impossible, many thanks for lovely Christmas and lovely presents. Papa took me aside, said Mama worried about me, this their first grandchild, must promise not to over-exert myself. Promised. Thanked them both, got with Mother into our car, station waggon following with luggage. Rain for first part of journey, thereafter dry. Longed to get home in daylight to give Mother clear view of house, but no hope of getting Afonso to hurry; after Almeirim gave up hope. Got to Reinaldo at dusk, saw ahead forest of little twinkling lights; got nearer, drove between little white houses all softly lamp-lit, with welcoming figures silhouetted in every doorway. Our house one long line of light from lamps on brackets along verandah; wonderful homecoming, couldn't have looked more beautiful; final happy touch, wood fires crackling in living room, own bedroom and Mother's bedroom. Mother quite overcome, said no hint in my letters of homely beauty of scene, the very picture of simple comfort. I said hoped she would say same when daylight revealed scene in greater detail.

Wednesday December 27th.

Went with Mother on inspection of house and precincts, stood in rain to watch Mother watching bread going into bread oven, went through puddles to orchard, followed everywhere by Viking, who happy at instant recognition of Mother as type of visitor who liked taking dogs for walks. Got Mother back to house at last, she took off mackintosh and said realised even more, today, how sketchy my letters, hadn't given her first idea of charm of place. Went on to say surprised I hadn't covered those iron bedsteads, so easy to do, you just made a sort of out-sized teacosy, covered it to match bedspread and slipped it over ugly iron. Surprised also that I hadn't hung those lovely local blankets on all doors leading to verandah, would have given colour and character. Even more surprised hadn't screened view of kitchen from living room, so simple to do, must ask carpenter to set about it. Also great pity that I hadn't got some of those low feeding troughs and placed them along one side of verandah with plants and flowers, would have taken rather bare look away, hadn't I been just a little lazy about making improvements? Said no, hadn't been lazy at all, and if she'd seen the house as it was when I first set eyes on it, she wouldn't say I'd done nothing to improve it. She said had only been suggesting few little finishing touches; I said few little finishing touches could wait until heavy luggage unpacked. She said of course, how selfish of her, had forgotten that I would be longing to see what she had brought out, but did I realise had written to ask for chutney and pickles and not a word about baby or Maternity clothes? Told her chutney and pickles and tinned beans, since Afonso's residence in England, his favourite foods, obtainable here but only at astronomical prices. Went into spare bedroom where heavy luggage arrayed, first trunk contained bottles and jars very thickly padded to prevent breakage. Next trunk disclosed steady stream of baby wear, plus nappies, mackintosh aprons to give baby bath, shawls knitted by Aunt Freda and Aunt Mary, coatees, pantees and bootees knitted by other members of family; Mother dictated list of donors, Afonso came in and said remainder of time before birth of baby would be spent by me in writing thank you letters. Saw Mother laying out large quantity of wool, she said to be knitted by herself and myself. Reminded her that I had never been able to master intricacies of knitting, didn't intend to start now; she said great joy and privilege to knit for one's baby, also good discipline for me, as inclined to be too impatient. This endorsed by Afonso. Maternity garments unpacked; went to own room to try on, found looked even worse on than off, experienced distinct chill on observing that still masses of room in all garments for further expansion, realised baby had another three months of growing to do, stared at self in glass and tried to imagine bulge as real live baby; couldn't imagine.

Saturday December 30th.

Party of local friends to meet Mother. Food prepared by Mother, Dulcelinda and self, set out on verandah; Viking, though now trained to distinguish between own food and ours, tied to verandah post in case forgot training. Very cold night, Mother said hadn't realised Portuguese winter so cold. Afonso said this nothing, wait until January and February.

Monday January 1st.

Made resolution to love and cherish Afonso, also to suppress irritation caused by Mother's unceasing energy in doing little finishing touches about house; also to learn to knit for baby. Superintended clearing-out of old kitchen cupboards to make room for nice new ones made by carpenter. Drove to village with Mother, found man who knew man who had waste marble suitable for using in making terrace outside verandah; found man, found marble, ordered marble, drove home in rainstorm.

Wednesday January 3rd.

Dinner at Jinny's, large party, was enjoying myself but made by Afonso to leave at early hour, as he said had had enough of Jinny. Asked Mother on way home if liked Jinny, Mother after hesitation said nice girl but rather tactless, some of her observations not likely to endear her to guests. Afonso said in own room that refused to go on trying to put up with Jinny for my sake, in future kindly refuse all invitations. Said never heard such selfish remark in all my life; decided would not love and cherish.

Saturday January 6th.

Unceasing rain, whiskers growing on everything, fires lit in all rooms to dry out.

Monday January 8th.

Unceasing rain. Mother said good weather to knit for baby, ludicrous that woman my age unable to make simple garments for own child. Took wool, took pattern, took needles, with Mother's help performed ceremony known as casting on, left to proceed and persevere. Proceeded and persevered, inspection by Mother revealed that what thought by me to be pretty pattern nothing but dropped stitches. Gave up knitting, said if didn't, baby would be born with wicked temper.

Saturday January 13th.

To Lisbon with Afonso and Mother, for Mama's birthday and for check-up. Nice sunny drive, no rain, took picnic lunch and ate it in clearing in woods. Bought flowers and handkerchiefs as present, went on to doctor's, baby still there. Dinner party for Mama, brightened by surprise appearance of Vasco who home for her birthday, after stopping with Maria and Jorge at Oporto and therefore doubly welcome as able to give latest news of them; reported that Jorge and Maria house-hunting, object of search not only nice house but also house not too near Jorge's mother, who I gathered very good very sweet interfering old cat.

Monday January 13th.

Afonso out with Papa; Mama, Mother and self shopped

for baby's cot, pram, bath and carry-cot. Before leaving for shopping expedition, awkward moment when taken by Mama up to old nursery and offered Afonso's old cot; took one look, decided quite impossible, reminded me of rickshaw entered for Battle of Flowers, said how lovely but didn't think suitable for Reinaldo, as Reinaldo either very dusty or very damp, shame to spoil lovely cot, why not offer to Jorge and Maria? Mama said would send to them. In shops, dispute, very polite, between Mama and Mother about who would pay for purchases; Mother won by quiet but firm announcement that my godfather's present to me. Said later that this in one way true; Uncle George having paid her fare, she could use money to buy baby's cot, etc.; present from him, even though oblique.

On way home to Reinaldo, asked Afonso if he had mentioned gas fridge to his father; he said had meant to, but had quite slipped out of his mind. I said hadn't far to slip. He asked Mother if she had noticed my temper getting very frayed at edges? Mother said natural at this time. I said if living with Afonso, natural at any time.

Saturday January 20th.

Break in rain; long drive with Mother and Afonso, object: to explore on Uncle George's behalf vicinity of Torres Vedras, to discover how many of old Peninsular War forts still visible. Arrived at Torres Vedras, Mother searched in handbag for map expressly drawn and marked by Uncle George. No map. Rest of drive agonised conjecture on Mother's part as to whether left it at home at Reinaldo or at home in England.

Saturday January 27th.

Pouring rain. Afonso unable to put off drive to Abrantes on business; said would take Mother if she wanted to go, but not me, as road beyond Abrantes bad for baby. Prepared nice picnic for them to eat in car on way, waved them off, heard phone, answered it and heard Jinny saying hadn't Afonso gone off to Abrantes? so had Manuel, could she come and spend day? Said delighted. Put receiver down, phone rang, heard voice which at first didn't recognise as Gustavo's; said he was desperate, Elisa in labour, wanted to see me, could I come? Said would come at once, got out Land Rover, saw Jinny coming, told her news, Jinny said we would go in her car, as faster. Added that Gustavo no business to ask me and Elisa no business to ask him to ask me. Didn't answer this, as several peals of thunder. Jinny asked what had touched off baby, said didn't know. Arrived at house; Gustavo distraught. Told us he had wanted to send for neighbouring mothers of experience, but Elisa only wanted me; local retired midwife sent for in case doctor not in time; doctor, with Elisa's parents, now on way from Tomar. Learned that Elisa had slipped in bathroom, no apparent damage at time but only too clear later. Taken by Gustavo to bedroom and left alone with Elisa; she said that thought she was about to die, but happy if I would promise to look after Gustavo and baby. Sat on bed, said if about to die, most practical step would be to draw up suitable list of second wives for Gustavo, but statistics showed that large proportion of mothers survived birth of premature babies, and if she wanted to know my present sentiments, they were pure envy. Gustavo came in, I got up to go, Elisa said no, would like me to stay, apologised for selfishness in having me with her at this time but immense comfort not to say support. Light meal organised by Jinny and sent up. Went downstairs, Jinny and Gustavo lunching, Jinny eating well, Gustavo crying. Jinny said that had heard servants say that large tree down on road from Tomar, shouldn't Gustavo take her car and go and investigate? Could if necessary tranship Elisa's mother and father and doctor. Gustavo next seen driving Jinny's car through sheet of mud, I asked Jinny where was fallen tree? She said no fallen tree, but essential to get Gustavo out of way, as about to disintegrate, this bad for Elisa. I said, when recovered from shock, but Good Heavens, suppose Elisa died while he was away? Jinny said suppose she didn't? far more likely to die with Gustavo already in mourning. I said husband's place beside wife. Jinny said this depended entirely on husband's ability to stand up under strain; if Gustavo support for Elisa, why had Elisa sent for me? Went upstairs, prayed Elisa wouldn't ask for Gustavo, relieved to find no mention. Sat by her, but couldn't think of anything to do but rub her hands and put damp handkerchiefs on head. She said would I pray? I said only able offer Protestant prayers, should I ask for boy or girl? Heard her say would rather not have Gustavo in room at this time.

Tried to count time, watch stopped, no clock in bedroom,

wondered why midwife didn't come up, remembered had asked me to tell her when required, decided that required now, went out to landing and sent waiting maid to fetch. Heard car, saw with thankfulness swift disembarkation of Elisa's father and mother, followed by doctor, followed to my surprise by family priest. Went downstairs, heard Jinny directing mother, father and doctor upstairs and priest into drawing room. Heard car, saw Gustavo getting out of Jinny's behind parents' car, from which descending two Portuguese nurses and man introduced as anaesthetist. Saw also arriving ambulance with crew. Gustavo said obstruction on road fortunately cleared, had seen parents' car and turned and followed them. Sounds from above indicated that doctor only just in time.

Baby born at 6.40 p.m. Though premature, looked to me very well finished, though with malignant expression. Elisa spent but safe, Gustavo in tears, this time of relief. Elisa carried down to ambulance, she, baby, doctor, anaesthetist and nurses departed to Tomar, followed by parents in own car. Jinny took me home, said wouldn't come in, must go back and tell Manuel how lucky they were to avoid this kind of trouble. No sign of Mother or Afonso; decided would have dinner in bed, was surprised to find knees rather shaky, glad to lie down. Ate soup and fish and felt fine. Afonso and Mother came home, asked if had had nice quiet day, I said yes. After their dinner, heard phone, heard Afonso answer, heard him greet Gustavo. Thereafter, long silences punctuated by incredulous exclamations from Afonso. At end of phone call, pause, after which heard Mother and Afonso advancing towards bedroom. Decided wisest thing lock myself in bathroom. Did so.

Saturday February 24th.

To Lisbon for check-up; baby still there, only more so. Doctor gave probable date of arrival as March 15th. Mama said must come down from Reinaldo on 10th at latest. Went with her to Clinic, inspected plan of rooms, chose one with view of Tagus. On way back to house, she said had exciting piece of news, could I guess? Said no. She said about to announce Ana's engagement. I said oh how wonderful, who is he? Mama said didn't I remember that charming young man at Christmas, the one who sent flowers to her every day? Said no, didn't remember; made mental note to ask Afonso why no flowers for Mother every day when wooing me. Learned that Ana to live in Oporto after marriage, so nice for Maria. Very small family party for dinner, only sixteen, as Mama said wise for me to lead quiet life at present time. Dinner remarkable by reason of remark by Papa to effect that thinking of having electricity put into Reinaldo house in near future. Tried to make myself say would rather have gas fridge; said nothing. Afonso said later that very odd I hadn't expressed pleasure at Papa's announcement, what had I been thinking of? Said gas fridge. He said why gas fridge when soon electric fridge likely? I said electricity only mooted, was willing to bet no electricity until baby tall enough to reach switches, therefore gas bird in hand better than electric bird in bush.

Sunday February 25th.

Lunch party at house; sat next to Uncle Feliciano; he said hoped that if baby boy, would have Feliciano as one of names. Side-stepped this, told him I hoped would see him on visit to Reinaldo before my mother left for England; he said charmed to pay visit, had heard my food superlative. Said yes, since advent of gas stove. Pause; had blinding flash of inspiration, said that was now trying to persuade Afonso to install gas fridge, but so far without success. Drove back to Reinaldo after dinner, as Afonso appointment early on Monday morning.

Tuesday February 27th.

Drove with Mother to see Elisa, who back home with baby; her mother staying with her until end of March. Elisa fatter, baby flourishing though in my opinion and Mother's overclothed; general regret that owing to being boy, unable name after me.

Wednesday February 28th.

Large truck drew up outside house just as Afonso on way out after lunch. Invoice handed by driver to Afonso, who stared at it, stared at me and asked in dazed tone had I gone crazy? this gas fridge, had I ordered it? Said certainly not, never heard of such a thing, would I take step of that kind without consulting him? was probably surprise from Papa. Stood with

Afonso and Mother on steps of verandah watching wrappings stripped from load; beautiful white gas fridge disclosed, with label marked Love from Uncle Feliciano. Mother said oh how kind of him, what a charming gesture. Afonso, after thoughtful pause, asked me if I had by any remote chance happened to mention matter of gas fridge to Uncle Feliciano? Face saved by Mother, who instantly, in tone of surprise and indignation, said surely Afonso not insinuating that I had dropped hint? Afonso understood to say no, not insinuating. Fridge carried by delivery men into kitchen. Told Afonso in bed that night that nice thing about Our Lady, his Lady, was Her obvious ability to recognise essentials when asked for them.

Friday March 2nd.

Jinny came round to say goodbye, flying home to Florida to get dry. Gave me three lovely coatees for baby, also parcel of new books to be read in Clinic, said she would come back in time to visit me there and inspect baby, had I seen Elisa's? I said yes, sweet little thing. Jinny said must have my eyes examined; baby image of Gustavo.

Friday March 9th.

Went round house wondering when would see it again, if ever. Left instructions to dry out all linen whenever weather permitted, though at present no sign that rain will ever stop. Marble for terrace outside verandah piled outside verandah waiting for dry interval.

Saturday March 10th.

To Lisbon with Mother and Afonso, own luggage, baby's luggage, Mother's luggage but not Afonso's, as he merely taking me to Lisbon, leaving me there and returning on 14th to await arrival of baby.

Monday March 13th.

Last visit to doctor, who said baby poised for neat dive into world. Inspected room at Clinic, which now empty and awaiting me.

Tuesday March 14th.

Afonso arrived in time for dinner, didn't think I could be so happy to see anyone. He said must arrange for baby to be born on his birthday on 21st.

Tuesday March 21st.

Afonso's birthday, no baby.

Wednesday March 22nd.

Went to bed as usual, got pain, said didn't think baby pain, but Afonso convinced labour begun; got up, dressed, wrapped me up, left message for Mama and Mother, drove me to Clinic.

Thursday March 23rd.

Drove me home again; doctor said not in labour.

Saturday March 25th.

Got pains, Afonso convinced baby but thought advisable ask Mama. Woke Mama, Mama said must go at once; Afonso dressed, wrapped me up, drove me to Clinic.

Sunday March 26th.

Drove me back again, no labour; he said business of birth very ill-managed, why not better communication between mother and baby instead of only guesswork?

Monday March 27th.

Woke up about midnight, pains in back, thought better say nothing yet, too humiliating to shuttle to and from Clinic. Pains worse but still bearable, wondered whether had better wake Afonso. Pains much worse, decided much better to be a man and not go through this. Tried to time pains, couldn't, decided at last to wake Afonso. Woke him. He said was I quite sure this time, so humiliating to shuttle to and from Clinic. Said was quite sure. He said had better consult Mama. Went to fetch Mama. Mama said yes, must go at once. Afonso said yes, but was mistaken last time, ought to ask my mother. Went to fetch Mother. Mother came, took one look, said how dare Afonso delay so long, Afonso said no delay, only making sure,

Mama said had urged him to go, but he wouldn't, Mother said quite impossible to expect men to use imagination at time like this, Afonso said tired of being told by Clinic staff that no baby, only hysteria. Dressed, wrapped me up, drove me to Clinic.

Wednesday March 29th.

Son born yesterday, 28th, weighed in kilogrammes, converted found to be 8 lb. 2 oz. Dark, like Afonso; malignant expression, like Elisa's baby. Mama says like Papa. Mother says like Uncle George. Afonso says like me. Afonso came in hour ago, kissed me, went into adjoining room to see baby, came back to report sleeping peacefully next to little English girl. I said in that case, had better name him Vasco.

Monday April 3rd.

Lovely day, marred by arguments regarding:

1.   Length of my stay in Clinic. Mama said four weeks. Mother said three weeks. I said two weeks was two weeks too long, why couldn't I get up and go out and resume life? Afonso, appealed to, said would think it over. While thinking it over, was presented by cashier with bill for first week's stay at Clinic plus doctor's fee plus anaesthetist's fee plus injections fee plus several other pluses. Afonso, when recovered from shock, said in voice brooking no opposition from anybody that I could leave the place as soon as I liked, in fact sooner. Leaving date fixed for Tuesday 11th.

2.Baby's Christening. Afonso said Papa and Mama would like to have Christening on Saturday 7th. I said in alarm, why so early? anything wrong with health of baby? Afonso said no, no, no, baby strong as horse, but Catholic Christenings merely religious ceremonies and not usually occasions for parties; also no need for me to be present unless I wanted to. I said had he gone crazy? Why wouldn't I want to be present at Christening of my own baby? Afonso said only baby, godparents and priest concerned. I said nobody was going to christen my baby without me, and there was going to be a party afterwards. Afonso said parties not usual, wouldn't guests think I had Christening presents in view? I said hadn't had, but now he came to mention it, party more desirable than ever. Date fixed for Saturday 15th, invitations to be sent out to members of family.

3.Name of baby. I said baby would be named Jorge after my uncle, and Vasco after Vasco. Continued to say this until general agreement reached.

4.Question of nurse for baby. Mama said had interviewed several possibilities, of course she and Papa only too anxious, not to say happy to pay salary, but essential to have trustworthy trained woman. I said had decided to look after baby myself while still breast-feeding as in any case impossible to leave him for longer than four hours at stretch; when milk showed signs of lessening, would look out for reliable girl either from Reinaldo or Tomar, and train her; very grateful to Papa and Mama, but didn't want regular Nanny, at any rate not yet.

Mama disposed to argue, but Afonso strongly on my side. Am to be permitted to look after own baby.

Tuesday April 4th.

Visit from Gustavo and Elisa; baby admired, said to be like me. Elisa said hoped to have me back at Reinaldo soon, missed me very much. Presented baby with little woolly hat; said thank you, didn't add that weather now too warm for little woolly hats.

Saturday April 8th.

Visits from members of family; welcome reappearance of Jinny, who like ray of light in beautiful primrose-coloured suit. She said Manuel left at home as very busy; longed to have me back at Reinaldo, as missed me very much, nobody else who spoke her language. Presented baby with little woolly horse, said what a good thing baby Northern type, was it hell having it and if so, perhaps a good thing as would prevent me from making a habit of it, must go now as could see Afonso coming and couldn't bear that smug expression on his face, did he think he had had the baby?

Tuesday April 11th.

Back at Mama's house. Both Mama and Mother anxious to get me to stay in bed; said no, would go to bed early and take things quietly, but would not, repeat not continue to lie up or lie down.

Had baby put in cot on my side of bed. Afonso woke when baby cried for night feed; stayed awake, very attentive, very loving.

Thursday April 13th.

Afonso suggested having baby in dressing room at night.

Friday April 14th.

Afonso said impossible for him to get decent night's rest when wakened by baby's howls; added was sorry that I was obliged to get up and cope with situation, but in circumstances nothing he could do to assist; wasn't there any way a mother could know the baby was hungry before baby actually said so?

Saturday April 15th.

Vasco and Inez arrived to be godparents; told Afonso I thought they would make a good pair, didn't he think so? He said on the whole, no. House began to fill with relations; realised that Mama, after slow start, had warmed to the idea of Christening party. Church full but ceremony rather untidy, as nobody sat down; priest, godparents and priest's assistant proceeded with Service while everybody else fidgeted on fringe. Service beautiful and picturesque, marred for me by unsuitable appearance of priest's assistant, small boy of about twelve dressed in unclean flannel trousers and uncleaner football sweater. Complained about this to Afonso, who said hadn't noticed and didn't think it mattered anyway, added that after seeing Vasco and Inez in Church, thought after all they might make a good pair, only how to disentangle Vasco from unknown number of unknown girls?

Back to lovely Christening cake and champagne; several presents, all to Afonso's relief of the small, baby-wear kind; sole exception diamond-studded medallion from Uncle Feliciano. Asked Mother whether she had enjoyed Christening; this in view of fact that Jorge had been christened not in my old christening robe, but in that worn by Papa, Papa's forbears as well as Afonso, Duarte, José, Vasco, Alberto, Maria, Ana, Valeria, Francisco and Luiz. She said had enjoyed it very much, and thought actual ceremony full of beauty and imagination. Thought of repeating this to Papa to please him; didn't, as not quite clear what meant by imagination.

Sunday April 16th.

Raised matter of returning to Reinaldo. Mama upset, said can't bear to think of our going. Mother turned scales by saying she must leave for England at end of month at latest; went on to suggest, to my surprise not to say dismay, that Mama came back to Reinaldo with us for short visit, to settle baby in. Asked her later why, she said because Jorge Mama's first grandchild, just as her first grandchild, and she had felt selfish going back to Reinaldo with us and having Jorge all to herself and leaving poor Mama behind.

Tuesday April 18th.

Left after breakfast for Reinaldo after long argument as to best means of travel. I said would sit beside Afonso in our car, and hold baby; Mother and Mama said this out of question, uncomfortable for baby, exhausting for me; far better to go in big car or even in station waggon, though this full of baby's cot, pram, bath and etceteras. Afonso said why not put baby in carry-cot in small compartment at back of front seats of our car? Mama and Mother said out of question, as terrible draught, unfelt by us in front seats, would blow on baby throughout journey, causing cold in nose, cold in eyes, cold in ears and double pneumonia. Afonso said this risk quite easily overcome: we would drive with all windows closed. Set off in own car, with baby and closed windows. At Vila Franca, morning's rain stopped, sun came out, car got warm, Afonso opened window. I said must shut at once on account of cold in nose, cold in eyes, cold in ears and double pneumonia. Afonso shut window, drove on to Almeirim with windows closed, temperature of car rose to roasting point, Afonso opened window, said roasting baby worse than freezing baby. I said couldn't drive knowing baby being blown on by terrible draughts. Afonso said in that case he would crawl into back compartment and baby could drive. Argument settled by my taking baby out of cot and holding on knee, self and baby very happy and comfortable, and feeding time greatly simplified, as Afonso merely drove on while I draped shawl modestly over shoulder and acted part of maternal fount. Got home well ahead of big car and station waggon. Given heart-warming welcome by staff, hangers-on and Viking. Afonso took baby in arms and circulated proudly, showing off; self unregarded on outskirts of crowd until Afonso suddenly remembered that baby had two parents. Viking discouraged from licking, nuzzling or pawing baby. Baby installed in bedroom next to ours; Mother and Mama put in rooms at other end of house. Went early to bed, told Afonso that hadn't realised how much had been longing to be back at Reinaldo. He said that went for him, too; added as grace note that had been longing to be back at Reinaldo with me.

Thursday April 20th.

Weather heavenly, warm, sunny, Springlike. After morning feed, put Jorge in pram out on verandah under light coverings. Mama came out, added two shawls and a blanket. Mother came out, said oh what lovely morning, why was baby smothered in so many coverings on so beautiful a day? Took off everything but one blanket. Mama said this very dangerous, baby far too new, far too tender, far too fragile as yet for exposure to elements. Mother said no elements, only sun-drenched verandah, lucky baby to have such nice climate to thrive in. Mama said little babies unable to generate own warmth, put on two more blankets. Mother took off again, said to Mama in kind but firm voice that English babies renowned throughout world for beautiful skins and healthy bodies, this not possible if coddled or cossetted. Mama pointed out that this not

English baby. Mother said only had to look at baby to see had inherited all English tendencies not say characteristics. Mama said gently that must forgive her, but had brought up ten children in this climate, which very treacherous; put on shawl and two blankets. Maid, with unsuspected finesse, came to say coffee ready in living room. Mother came to my room at next baby-feed, said Mama best of mothers-in-law, kind and generous and affectionate, but I must remember always that Portuguese were Portuguese and smothering babies never did them any good. When I was putting Jorge back on verandah, Mama came out and put two more blankets on, said my Mother very good very sweet but unhappily had not had ten children to bring up in Portugal, didn't understand climate, not to say Portuguese babies.

Saturday April 22nd.

Glorious day. Put Jorge outside in sunshine. Mother took off blankets, Mama put on blankets. Mama said baby could not, should not, must not be out of doors without little woolly cap; put on little woolly cap. Mother came out, saw little woolly cap, said oh dear me, didn't know it was snowing, took off little woolly cap. Mama came out, said must forgive her, didn't really agree with baby being outside at all at so tender an age, but as outside, head must at all costs be protected; put on little woolly cap. Mother said in protesting voice that this not depth of Arctic winter, but balmy Portuguese Spring. Mama said baby not interested in geography, only in protective covering on poor little head; put on woolly cap at more jaunty angle. Situation saved by God-sent appearance of Afonso, riding in to lunch. Told him after lunch that couldn't stand much more of this English-baby, Portuguese-baby, and had he noticed that my Mother, since coming back to Reinaldo, hadn't once mentioned having to leave for England at end of month? He said all I had to do was assert myself; baby after all mine and not Mother's or Mama's; all I had to do was be firm. After afternoon feed, put Jorge on verandah, covered him up, told Mother and Mama firmly that would be grateful if didn't interfere with coverings. Happened to pass pram later, saw two more blankets on baby. Took them off. Went past pram at tea time, saw Jorge with only one thin shawl over him; put on two blankets. Told Afonso in own bedroom after dinner that if either his mother or my Mother didn't go, I would go crazy.

Sunday April 23rd.

Afonso and Mama at Mass. While I was giving Jorge bath and feed, Mother came in and said must take this opportunity to talk with me. I said talk what about? She said about grandmothers; went on to say that I must always accord Mama respect and affection, but must also remember that the baby mine and not Mama's, and I must on no account resign my position as mother of baby. Long pause, during which I summoned up enough courage to say that my view of how to bring up baby seemed to be midway between Mama's and hers. After another long pause, during which hadn't liked to look at Mother, heard her saying quietly that this was the point she had come to make: the differences in grandmothers; between herself and Afonso's mother there was perhaps one very important difference indeed, which was that while she, Mother, was ready and willing to learn, it was not really likely that Afonso's mother would ever change her views or her ways. What was more, grandmothers, though of great use as baby-sitters, baby-petters and refuges-in-time-of-trouble, were not really competent to advise young mothers. Experience? Well yes, that counted for something, but when you really came down to it, it didn't count for much in the face of twenty or twenty-five years of change and progress. If the baby's mother was twenty or twenty-five years ahead of her own mother in outlook, why shouldn't the baby start off twenty or twenty-five years ahead, instead of having to grow up on his grandmother's outworn ideas? Pause. I felt tears trickling down nose; unable to wipe off as dealing with baby. Mother wiped them away and said she would like to tell me something she had never told anybody, and that was that poor Aunt Freda had made a terrible mess of being a grandmother. She, Mother, had watched, had looked on and had promised herself that never, never would she make the same mistakes— yet here she was, with Jorge not a month old, already guilty of interference. Pause to wipe my tears, then went on to say that ever since my father died, she had faced the thought of losing me; faced it cheerfully because when I left her, I would be going to a full and happy life of my own. People said that partings came when the bride went away; in her, Mother's, opinion, this wasn't so. The real parting came, as it had come with us now, when the bride was a mother in her own right and had to bring up her children her own way. She had to admit that she was of the old school; she didn't believe in vitamin drops, anti-T.B. injections, anti-whooping-cough, anti-measles, solids at three months or excessive sun bathing; she believed in mother's milk, Scott's emulsion and God's grace. So did poor Aunt Freda. But Aunt Freda's daughters had only believed in Doctor Spock. If I thought that she, Mother, was going back to the cottage to a life of repining and loneliness, I was doing her a great injustice. She was going back to a full and, she hoped, useful life. If her life was only to depend on seeing me and my children, she didn't really feel it would be much of a life; she wanted one of her own, apart from us. She loved me and Afonso and Jorge and would save up and come out and see us, and hoped we would come and stay with her, but all she wanted at this moment, loving us as she did, was to go away before spoiling the happy relationship that had always existed between us. She felt very sorry for poor Mama, who was going to stay here and get more and more on my nerves by interfering in matters that had nothing to do with her.

Afonso came home with Mama and said Mama had been talking to him seriously, and was sorry she had put a woolly cap on the baby when I wasn't looking, hoped I would forgive her.

Papa telephoned in evening: had to go to Oporto on business, would Mama and my mother care to drive up with him? Good opportunity for my mother to see something of the north of Portugal before leaving for England. Mother said delighted to go, so kind of Papa.

Tuesday April 25th.

Mother and Mama left for Lisbon. Not final goodbye to Mother, as stopping on way back from Oporto in order to take another look at Jorge and collect luggage. Stood with Afonso watching car drive away, tried not to cry, cried. Afonso said had I any regrets? I said only one: a deep and terrible one at watching my Mother go away and understanding that it was better for us both, and better for the baby and better for Afonso that she should go, and that even if I could have gone with her, I wouldn't have been able to bring myself to leave my husband, my son and my lovely home. Afonso kissed me, said loved me more and more and would always love and cherish, added that as nobody now in end bedroom, wouldn't it be a good idea to put Jorge in there at night?

THE END

The Gentlemen Go By

by

Elizabeth Cadell

"Oh—Florence!" Lorna turned and called, and Florence, on her way into the house, paused and glanced over her shoulder.

"Well?"

"You didn't tell me his name," said Lorna.

"Nicholas."

"Yes," said Lorna, "but there must be some more."

"Nicholas Saracen," said Florence, and went into the house.

And Lorna Salvador, on the terrace, stared after her with the blood draining slowly from her face and her eyes wide and filled with something not far from panic.

Nicholas . . . Nicholas Saracen. He was coming here. He was coming . . . soon . . . now. She would be face to face with him; she would see him, hear him, be near enough to touch him. She felt herself trembling at the thought, and made a desperate attempt to regain her self-command. She forced herself to look forward, and saw their meeting as it would be—a young man coming to meet an unknown woman, a young man anxious to talk about himself and his life. Nicholas—in love. Nicholas, Nicholas, Nicholas—

The moments passed, but Lorna stood still, quieter now, and with a new feeling welling up from the bottom of her heart. Nicholas—she was free to see him. That was all that she need think about at present. A smile curved her lips; it was tremulous at first, but it grew wider; a light of expectancy came into her eyes and the colour came back to her cheeks. She found herself free from apprehension, and lifted up with pure happiness. Nicholas . . .

Joyously, she went inside to prepare for his arrival.

❦

End of preview.

To continue reading, look for the book entitled "The Gentlemen Go By" by Elizabeth Cadell.

About the Author

Elizabeth Vandyke was born in British India at the beginning of the 20th century. She married a young Scotsman and became Elizabeth Cadell, remaining in India until the illness and death of her much-loved husband found her in England, with a son and a daughter to bring up, at the beginning of World War 2. At the end of the war she published her first book, a light-hearted depiction of the family life she loved. Humour and optimism conquered sorrow and widowhood, and the many books she wrote won her a wide public, besides enabling her to educate her children (her son joined the British Navy and became an Admiral), and allowing her to travel, which she loved. Spain, France and Portugal provide a background to many of her books, although England and India were not forgotten. She finally settled in Portugal, where her married daughter still lives, and died when well into her 80s, much missed by her 7 grandchildren, who had all benefitted from her humour, wisdom and gentle teaching. British India is now only a memory, and the quiet English village life that Elizabeth Cadell wrote about has changed a great deal, but her vivid characters, their love affairs and the tears and laughter they provoke, still attract many readers, young and not-so-young, in this twenty-first century. Reprinting these books will please her fans and it is hoped will win her new ones.

Also by Elizabeth Cadell

My Dear Aunt Flora
Fishy, Said the Admiral
River Lodge
Family Gathering
Iris in Winter
Sun in the Morning
The Greenwood Shady
The Frenchman & the Lady
Men & Angels
Journey's Eve
Spring Green
The Gentlemen Go By
The Cuckoo in Spring
Money to Burn
The Lark Shall Sing
Consider The Lilies
The Blue Sky of Spring
Bridal Array
Shadow on the Water
Sugar Candy Cottage
The Green Empress
Alice Where Art Thou?
The Yellow Brick Road
Six Impossible Things
Honey For Tea
The Language of the Heart
Mixed Marriage

Letter to My Love
Death Among Friends
Be My Guest
Canary Yellow
The Fox From His Lair
The Corner Shop
The Stratton Story
The Golden Collar
The Past Tense of Love
The Friendly Air
Home for the Wedding
The Haymaker
Deck With Flowers
The Fledgling
Game in Diamonds
Parson's House
Round Dozen
Return Match
The Marrying Kind
Any Two Can Play
A Lion in the Way
Remains to be Seen
The Waiting Game
The Empty Nest
Out of the Rain
Death and Miss Dane

199

Afterword

Note: Elizabeth Cadell is a British author who wrote her books using the traditional British spelling. Therefore because these books are being published worldwide, the heirs have agreed to keep her books exactly as she wrote them and not change the spelling.

Printed in Great Britain
by Amazon

42135607R00116